The True Story of Simon Girty, the Renegade
By **TIMOTHY TRUMAN**

Book 1: The Borderland

WILDERNESS

WILDERNESS tm
— BOOK 1: THE BORDERLAND tm

Published by:
4Winds Publishing Group, Inc.
P.O. Box 5208
Lancaster, Pa. 17601 U.S.A.

First Printing:
December 1989

Hardcover:
ISBN 0-922173-06-0 ($19.95)
Trade Paperback:
ISBN 0-922173-05-2 ($12.95)
Signed Hardcover:
ISBN 0-922173-11-7 ($59.95)
BIOGRAPHY/ILLUSTRATED BOOK

Author and Illustrator:
TIMOTHY TRUMAN
Letterer:
Timothy Harkins
Publishers:
Charles Dixon & Timothy Truman
Sales Representative:
Stephen Scott Smith
Associate Editor:
Michael H. Price

Printed in the U.S.A. at Acorn
Press, Lancaster, Pa.

For distribution or licensing information
contact Timothy Truman or Charles Dixon
at 4Winds Publishing Group, Inc.,
P.O. Box 5208,
Lancaster, Pa., U.S.A. 17601
(717) 569-0612 or (304) 453-2008

Author's Note

Wilderness is the story of Simon Girty, who was born in 1741 in Northeastern Pennsylvania and died in 1818 at seventy-seven years of age as an exile in Canada.

In relating his tale, *Wilderness* also must tell the story of the wars that raged among the native tribes of the Eastern and Midwestern United States and the white colonizers who sought to settle upon tribal North American lands.

Many among us who are unfamiliar with the era find it difficult to understand that during much of Girty's life the frontier — the wilderness — began at the banks of the Ohio River. Westward lay the villages of nearly a dozen native tribes. To the South — in West Virginia and Kentucky — were found the rich tribal hunting grounds that these peoples shared. The forests there were gardens of abundance upon which the native peoples of the Eastern and Midwestern United States depended for their families to live and their civilization to prosper. Until the seventeen-seventies, few Europeans had entered these lands; but as the whites outgrew their Eastern settlements, their numbers spilled beyond the Ohio in an uncontrolled flood.

A still more disappointing and troublesome misunderstanding of history is that most Americans who were raised on Hollywood's cowboys-and-Indians version of the Westward movement do not comprehend the magnitude of the warfare that was waged between the Europeans and the Native Americans in the Eastern half of the United States. This war lasted for nearly one hundred years. Somehow, it was not communicated to many of us that the American Revolution was fought not only in Bunker Hill and Germantown but also in the wilderness around Pittsburgh, Pennsylvania, and Wheeling, West Virginia, and Lexington, Kentucky. The combatants in these instances were not uniformed soldiers, waging war beneath unfurled banners to the accompaniment of skirling fifes. No, the wilderness war was a guerilla war of stealth and surprise, raids and ambushes. As had the French before them, the British found that they could transform the native tribes' fear of white encroachment into a weapon of hideous force. When the Revolutionary War ended in 1783, it ended only for the white combatants on the Eastern Seaboard. In the dark forests beyond the Ohio, the fighting between red men and white men continued with only brief respite for thirty years more.

The life of Simon Girty spanned much of this period. He lived through the French and Indian War, Pontiac's "Rebellion," Lord Dunmore's War, the American Revolution, the Post-Revolutionary Indian Wars of the Ohio Valley, and the War of 1812. His entire life was affected by — and intricately linked with — each conflict.

Every episode depicted in this book is based upon documented evidence. While I have included scattered transitional sequences to ensure a smooth narrative flow between certain episodes, I have taken only few liberties for the sake of dramatic contrivance. Mr. Girty's life contains drama enough.

Whenever possible, I have employed actual dialogue as was reported at the time. Any other dialogue has been constructed only in light of the careful study of the events portrayed and the nationalities, personalities, and apparent intentions of the principals.

In the case of the trader George Morgan's letter to his wife (found in Part No. 2, pages 27 and 28), this correspondence is for the most part an amalgam taken from several actual letters from Morgan to his spouse and from reports to his business partners, John Baynton and Samuel Wharton. All information that Morgan gives in this letter represents either his actual remarks or information that he certainly would have known about his faithful employee and, later, his devoted friend, Simon Girty.

Most of the major events in the life of Mr. Girty are fully documented in any number of published and archival accounts. A frustrating gap in his story occurs following the torture and death of his step-father, when Simon was taken from his mother and adopted into the Seneca tribe. Little is known about him during the nearly four years he spent in their villages. I have found it necessary, therefore, to rely on the numerous published accounts of other captive white settlers who were similarly abducted and then adopted by the Indians. In my efforts to determine parallels among their experiences, particularly helpful were the narratives of O.M. Spencer, James Ward, Col. James Smith, and John McCullough, and the reminiscences of Simon Kenton as collected by Edna Kenton. Also useful were the writings of the missionary John Heckewelder, who lived with these tribes and painstakingly chronicled their day-to-day culture and traditions. Most of the Indian languages used in the present book also are taken from his work. (You will meet the Rev. Mr. Heckewelder in these pages; his path crossed Girty's many times.)

The illustrations also demanded an incredible amount of research. When I am reading a book or watching a movie that concerns a subject with which I am acquainted, nothing frustrates me more than to notice the appearance of an object that is totally out of its time or place. If I doubt the appearance of that one object, then I find myself doubting the authenticity of the entire story. I have therefore tried my best to make certain that every article of clothing, every dwelling, every rifle, musket, pot, pan, batteau, and shoe buckle is appropriate to the time and the place.

I have chosen to use the graphic-story form to relate Mr. Girty's tale because it presents the most effective, most evocative means for me to take you into his world and to show you what happened to him. You can stay in that world — and with Simon Girty — as long as you want (or at least as long as there's a candle in the house).

This method of storytelling has presented me with a special challenge that would have been absent had I chosen to tell Simon Girty's story in conventional prose. Every page of *Wilderness* is composed of, on the average, six illustrations. Every one of these illustrations features a subject (if not several subjects) that required research for accuracy's sake. If the subject of the illustration is a human figure, I have attempted to make certain that the clothing is absolutely authentic and, moreover, correct for the year, the season, the culture, and the region depicted. If a person is armed, I have for example felt it necessary to prevent the intrusion of Post-Revolutionary War-style longrifles into scenes from the French and Indian War. In period illustrations such as these, it is best not to clothe Scots-Irish settlers in fashions associated with the Pennsylvania Germans. I know from personal experience that the rolling hills around the Juniata River, where Girty was raised, are by far different from the steep mountain trails of the Kanawha River that he climbed with Simon Kenton. For every scene that I drew, hundreds of elements required checking for accuracy.

The casual reader might consider it unimportant to labor over such minutiae. People who are well acquainted with such things, however, will find these details very, very important; any assumption to the contrary, any lapse of painstaking depiction, would severely interfere with their enjoyment of and belief in the story. When I began, it was with the commitment that some of my readers would learn here about people of whom we were never told in school — and about an era of bitter frontier warfare of which such tomes as *The American Heritage History of the United States* allow only passing mention. But I wanted also to give people who are familiar with the age a chance to enter it and have a look around. I am hopeful that they will find everything where it should be; if not, I feel certain they will let me know.

To supply a complete listing of the historical works that were used to construct an accurate portrait of Simon Girty's career and era, I have included a bibliography.

There are two books in the *Wilderness* series:

■ *The Borderland* follows Girty's life from birth to his involvement during the American Revolution with the British and their Indian allies.

■ And *Bloody Ground* tells in the main of the Ohio Valley Indian Wars following the Revolution and Girty's exile in Canada as a hated, crippled blind man.

Wilderness represents the first book-length study of Simon Girty to appear since 1928. Some of the information I have collected has not appeared in any previous biography. Of the four book-length biographies written about him prior to 1928, only one presents an extremely thorough and conspicuously documented look at his life. Except for the brief historical notes by A. Monroe Aurand, Jr., in the limited-edition reprinting of U.J. Jones' wholly fictional potboiler *Simon Girty: The Outlaw*, none of these biographies has shown the "White Savage" much sympathy. At the worst, Consul Wilshire Butterfield, who was at once Girty's most careful biographer and most relentless posthumous opponent, described the man as "a ... brutal, depraved, and wicked ... monster of cruelty" and a "dark whirlwind of fury, desperation, and savagery."

My *Wilderness* does not paint Simon Girty as a villain. Neither have I sought to whitewash him as a freedom-fighting hero. I have only examined the very evidence that Butterfield and other biographers first presented in their own works, but with eyes less clouded by the era of Manifest Destiny in which they lived and the tunnel vision and unfortunate racism that it bred.

Nor have I taken what I believe is the equally racist and simplistic stance that would picture most Westward-moving whites as a merciless horde whose main purpose was to subjugate or destroy a race of noble (and, in effect, all too childlike and helpless) forest-dwellers who lived in a perfect Utopia until the white man came.

What I *have* sought to portray is a time when the New World was any land west of the Ohio River — a place populated with cultures that were tragically reluctant to understand one another. *Wilderness* pivots on two races of very brilliant, very different people who found themselves swirling in a cyclone agitated by their own dynamics. Both of these races were capable of the greatest acts of love and the most horrendous displays of brutality. In that regard, they were wholly — and equally — human.

Caught somewhere in this storm and in that wilderness was a man named Simon Girty.

Acknowledgments

Many people have assisted me in the *Wilderness* project. Their contributions ranged from helping to locate valuable research materials to providing unflagging support for the story I wanted to tell and for the way I chose to tell it. I owe these friends my undying gratitude.

■ Thanks to educators and good buddies **Edward Hamme** and **Kermit "Doc" Norris** for the questions they asked and the enthusiasm they showed from the very beginning, and for their company along the trail to "Points Girty" in Pennsylvania, West Virginia, Ohio, and Kentucky during the summers of 1988 and 1989. Finer companions were never had.

■ Thanks to **Stephen Scott "Beau" Smith** for the hours he spent in his hometown library of Huntington, West Virginia, tracking down local and state histories dealing with the Girty legend, and for understanding the spirit of the book and the mountain folk involved in Girty's story as only a fellow West Virginian could.

■ Thanks to my partner **Chuck Dixon**, who was as anxious to see the pictures and the story contained in the *Wilderness* books as I was.

■ Thanks to **Kim Yale** and **John Ostrander**, who have been in on this thing from the very beginning.

■ Thanks to all the other members of the infamous 4 Winds Gang and good-ol'-boy "conspiracy" — as fine a bunch of artists, writers, and reprobates as ever strutted this planet — for the inspiration, prodding, energy, and friendship they have always provided me.

■ Thanks to **Greg Walker** and **Verzell James** of the Associated Reading Service for their promotion of comic books and graphic stories as effective, entertaining, and powerful educational tools, and for their belief in this project and its purpose.

■ Special thanks to **Chief Halftown** of the Seneca Tribe for his suggestions concerning pictorial sources for Native American dress of the colonial period, and for offering cautionary words of wisdom in relation to the depiction of his tribe and their Eastern brothers. Thanks also to my friends, from tribes scattered across North America, who have written me about my past work, ever with words of support and appreciation for the way I have attempted to portray native peoples. I hope you enjoy this work, too.

■ Thanks to **John W.W. Loose** of the Lancaster [Pennsylvania] Historical Society, whose enthusiasm and scholarly wisdom led me to difficult-to-find archival materials, and who did much to set me along on the early steps of the trail.

■ Thanks to the various libraries and librarians who have assisted me in my efforts to understand the life, times, and mind of Simon Girty: The Lancaster [Pennsylvania] Public Library; the Pennsylvania State Library & Archives in Harrisburg; the Franklin & Marshall College Library; the Altoona [Pennsylvania] Area Public Library; the Huntington [West Virginia] Public Library; the Library of the University of Pittsburgh; and the Libraries of Edinboro University and Indiana University of Pennsylvania. Without their resources, this project would never have happened.

■ Thanks to the museums and historical societies I visited in an effort to collect various data, photographs, and even emotions for this work: The Campus Maritus Museum and Ohio River Museum in Marietta, Ohio; the Walnut Hill Cemetery and Betty Zane Memorial in Ohio; Fort Ticonderoga and Fort Crown Point in the State of New York; Bedford Village and the Fort Bedford Museum in Pennsylvania; the Landis Valley Farm Museum in Lancaster, Pennsylvania; the Edward Hand Plantation, also in Lancaster; Fort Hunter Museum, Brandywine Battlefield Museum, and the Conrad Weiser Homestead in Pennsylvania; Historic Washington Village, the Simon Kenton Shrine, Fort Harrod, and Fort Boonesboro in Kentucky. And a special thanks to the good folks at the Blue Licks Battlefield State Park in Kentucky. I hope that you, the reader, will support these and other historical landmarks in their efforts to keep our past preserved.

■ Thanks to White Savages **Fred Augello**, **Tom Yeates**, and **Arne Tillman**. Count coup, brothers!

■ Thanks to **Ken Dyer**, rifleman, who was one of the first to see my Girty drawings and tell me I was starting to get things "right," and whose enthusiasm for the illustrations made me feel right proud indeed. Also, to various other muzzle-loading rifle enthusiasts and historical re-enactors in the Lancaster, Pennsylvania, area, for hearing all my questions and making me feel at home.

■ Thanks to master gunmaker **C.G. Dixon**, who continues the art of building fine Pennsylvania longrifles, and whose critique of and comments on my drawings of frontier flintlocks accounted for one of the most enjoyable and educational experiences of this project.

■ Thanks to **Bill Lande**, **Joseph E. Sacca**, **Lynne Gilbert**, **Frank Cecala**, and all other participants and exhibitors at the annual Kempton [Pennsylvania] Muzzle-Loading Gunmakers Fair.

■ Thanks to **Robin McBride** for the research materials she so kindly sent (and for the Spirit Hawk pendant!)

■ Thanks to **Maria Coole** of the Lancaster *Sunday News* for her wonderfully perceptive article — and for being so genuinely moved to tears at the vision of Girty on the American Thames.

■ Thanks to illustrators **David Wright**, **Lou Glanzman**, and the late **Phillip Kappel**, whose paintings and drawings of frontier subjects make an enduring source of spirit, inspiration, and awe.

■ Thanks to the young historical artists **Lee Teter** and **Michelle Sweigert** for capturing the frontier in pencil and paint for a new generation.

■ Thanks to **Jack Jaxon**, **Sam Glanzman**, and **George E. Turner**, and to all the many others who, like them, have employed the graphic storytelling medium to tell their own true stories of history.

■ Thanks to brother **Phil Hoffman**, who is working on his own Girty biography. More so than any other historian, Phil has come up with the most logical and systematically worked-out answer to the question that has plagued the Girty legend for so long: Namely, *why* did Girty decide to leave Fort Pitt in 1778 to join the British and the Indians in Detroit? Phil's own volume will tackle this puzzle more carefully than I have been able to do here; I am extremely anxious to read that forthcoming book, *Victim: The Two Worlds of Simon Girty*. At any rate, I owe Phil a great debt of thanks — for sharing not only his reference resources but hours of telephone time, as well, as we passionately discussed the life of the complex man who had hammerlocked both our imaginations and would not — *will* not — let us go.

■ Thanks to the esteemed **Mr. Allan W. Eckert**, whose book *The Frontiersman* first caused me to question all those terrible stories we had been told about Simon Girty, and whose interest in my *Wilderness* and willingness to answer the questions I put to him proved all the greater reason to do a good piece of work.

■ Thanks to the **Truman** and **Steinman** clans, and to all their various affiliated branches, who made me feel I was up to something special with this one. And especially to my beloved **Beth**, **Ben**, and **Emily** — who suffered through almost two years of Daddy's "Girty-itis."

■ And finally, thanks to **A. Monroe Aurand, Jr.**, **Stephen Boyd**, **Consul Wilshire Butterfield**, **U.J. Jones**, **Charles McKnight**, and **T.L. Rodgers**, whose own writings on the Girty legend answered so many questions — and raised or let go unanswered just as many others.

For all you've done, my best. Any inaccuracies that might be found in this book are certainly not your doing.

—TIMOTHY TRUMAN
Lancaster, Pennsylvania

Bibliography

Primary Sources

Abernethy, T.P. *Western Lands and the American Revolution.* New York: 1959.

Arnow, H.S. *Seedtime in the Cumberland.* New York: 1960.

Aurand, A. Monroe, Jr. *Simon Girty, the Outlaw.* Harrisburg, Penna: 1931. (Biographical sketch and annotations to the reprinting of the 1846 book; see Jones, U.J.)

Bakeless, John. *Daniel Boone.* New York: 1939.

Baldwin, L.D. *Pittsburgh — The Story of a City.* Pittsburgh: The University of Pittsburgh, 1938.

Boyd, Thomas. *Mad Anthony Wayne.* New York: 1929.

Boyd, Thomas. *Simon Girty, the White Savage.* New York: 1928.

Butterfield, C.W. *History of the Girtys.* Cincinnati: 1890.

Darlington, W.W. *Christopher Gist's Journals — Historical, Geographical, and Ethnological Notes and Biographies of His Contemporaries.* New York: 1966. (Reproduction of the 1893 edition.)

De Haas, W. *History of the Early Settlement and Indian Wars of Western Virginia.* Wheeling, W. Va.: 1851.

Downes, R.C. *Council Fires of the Upper Ohio.* Pittsburgh: 1940.

Eckert, Allan W. *The Conquerors.* New York: 1970.

Eckert, Allan W. *The Frontiersman.* New York: 1967.

Eckert, Allan W. *Wilderness Empire.* New York: 1978.

Eckert, Allan W. *The Wilderness War.* New York: 1969.

Gray, E.E. and Gray, L.R. *Wilderness Christians* New York: Cornell University, 1956.

Graymont, B. *The Iroquois in the American Revolution.* Syracure, N.Y.: Syracuse University, 1972.

Hale, J.P. (Dudley, J.H., ed.) *Trans-Allegheny Pioneers (Third Edition).* Raleigh, N.C.: 1971.

Hartley, C.B. *Life and Adventures of Lewis Wetzel.* Philadephia: 1860.

Hassler, Edgar W. *Old Westmoreland.* Pittsburgh: 1900.

Hildreth, S.P. *Pioneer History — Being an Account of the First Examinations of the Ohio Valley and the Early Settlement of the Northwest Territory.* ——: 1848.

Horseman, R. *Matthew Elliott, British Indian Agent.* Detroit: 1964.

Jacob, John J. *Life of the Late Captain Michael Cresap.* Cincinnati: 1866.

Jones, U.J. *Simon Girty, the Outlaw.* Harrisburg, Penna.; 1931. (Limited-edition reprinting of the 1846 book; see *Aurand, A. Monroe, Jr.*)

Kelsay, I.T. *Joseph Brant, 1743-1807 — Man of Two Worlds.* Syracuse, N.Y.: Syracuse University: 1970.

Kenton, Edna. *Simon Kenton — His Life and Period.* Garden City, N.Y.: 1930.

McKnight, Charles. *Our Western Border.* Philadelphia: 1876.

Pritts, J. *Border Incidents.* Lancaster, Penna: 1841.

Savalle, Max. *George Morgan — Colony Builder.* New York: Columbia University, 1932.

Sipes, C.H. *Indian Wars of Pennsylvania.* Philadelphia: 1929.

Spencer, O.M. *The Captivity of O.M. Spencer.* Chicago: The Lakeside Press, 1917. (Limited-edition reprinting of the 1835 book.)

Sword, Wiley. *President Washington's Indian War — The Struggle for the Old Northwest, 1790-1795.* Norman, Okla.: The University of Oklahoma, 1985.

Thwaites, R.G., and Kellogg, L.P., eds. *Documentary History of Dunmore's War, 1774; The Revolution on the Upper Ohio, 1775-1777; Frontier Defense on the Upper Ohio, 1777-1778.* Madison, Wisc.: 1905-1912.

Wallace, A.F.C. *Death and Rebirth of the Seneca.* New York: 1969.

Wallace, Paul A.W. *The Travels of John Heckewelder in Frontier America.* Pittsburgh: 1958.

Withers, A.S. *Chronicles of Border Warfare.* Cincinnati: 1895.

Historical Society Collections

(Courtesy Lancaster, Penna., Historical Society)

Ohio: *Historical Collections of Ohio.* Philadelphia: 1892.

Pennsylvania: *History of Lancaster County,* Ellis & Evans. Lancaster, Penna.: 1883.

Pennsylvania: *Pennsylvania History,* Vols. No. 1, No. 6, No. 18.

Pennsylvania: *Historical Society of Pennsylvania,* Vols. No. 31, 32, 47, 58, 59.

Secondary Sources

Allman, C.B. *Lewis Wetzel.* Old Greenwich: 1977 (Devin-Adair reprint of the 1939 edition).

Daughters of the American Revolution. *Fort Duquesne and Fort Pitt.* Pittsburgh: 1918.

DeVoto, B. *The Course of Empire.* Boston: 1952.

Diverse Authorship. *Foxfire* Vols. Nos. 1-3. Garden City, N.Y.: 1972.

Diverse Authorship. *Rand McNally Road Atlas.* New York: 1989.

Edmunds, R.D. *The Shawnee Prophet.* Lincoln, Nebr.: The University of Nebraska, 1983.

Georg, F. (Spittal, W.G., ed.) *Scalping and Torture — Warfare Practices of the American Indians.* Ontario: Iroqrafts Reprint, 1985.

Graymant, B. *The Iroquois.* New York: 1988.

Hawke, D.F. *Everyday Life in Early America.* New York: 1988.

Johnson, P.G. *New River: The Early Settlement.* Pulaski, Va.: 1983.

Morgan, L.H. *League of the Iroquois.* Rochester, N.Y.: 1854.

Reiter, Edith S. *Marietta and the Northwest Territory.* Marietta, Ohio: 1986 edition.

Scamyorn, R. and Stienle, John. *Stockades in the Wilderness.* Dayton, Ohio: 1986.

Smithsonian Institute, The. *The Smithsonian Book of American Indians.* Washington, D.C.: 1986.

Tantaquidegon, G. *Folk Medicine of the Delaware and Related Algonkian Indians.* Harrisburg, Penna.: 1977.

Todish, T.J. *America's First World War: The French and Indian War, 1754-1763.* Ogden, Utah: 1987.

Van Every, D. *Ark of Empire, Company of Heroes, Forth into the Wilderness, The Final Challenge.* New York: 1961-1964.

White, J.M. *Everyday Life of American Indians.* New York: 1979.

Young, C.M. *Life and Times of Little Turtle.* Cincinnati: 1977.

Pictorial Reference

American Red Cross, The. *Canoeing.* Washington, D.C.: 1956.

Caraway, C. *Eastern Woodland Indian Designs.* Owings Mills, Md.: 1984.

Christofferson, D.J. *Batteau, Battoe — A Pictorial Collection,* Vols. No. 1 and No. 2. St. Paul: 1986.

Darling, A.D. *Red Coat and Brown Bess.* Ontario: 1970.

Dixon, C., Ehrig, D., and Miller, D. *The Art of Building the Pennsylvania Longrifle.* Kempton, Penna.. 1978.

Elting, Col. J.R., ed., and *The Company of Military Historians. Military Uniforms in America — The Era of the American Revolution: 1755-1795.* San Rafael, Calif.: 1974.

Fadala, S. *The Complete Black Powder Handbook.* Northfield, Ill.: 1974.

Gabor, R. *Costumes of the Iroquois.* Ontario: 1980.

Gehret, E.J. *Rural Pennsylvania Clothing.* York, Penna.: 1980.

Hamilton, T.M. *Colonial Frontier Guns.* Chadron, Nebr.: 1980.

Hamilton, T.M. *Firearms of the Frontier.* Chadron, Nebr.: 1976.

Hanson, C.E. *The Trade Rifle Sketchbook.* Chadron, Nebr.: 1979.

Hanson, Dr. J.A. *The Long Hunter Sketchbook.* Chadron, Nebr.:.1983.

Hartman, S., Hudson, G., and Lee, J. *Indian Clothing of the Great Lakes: 1740-1840.* Ogden, Utah: 1978.

Johnson, J.R. *Kentucky Rifles and Pistols: 1750-1850.* Columbus, Ohio: 1976.

Lindsay, M., and Pendleton, B. *The Kentucky Rifle.* York, Penna.: 1972.

Nuemann, C.G., and Woodbridge, G. *History of Weapons of the American Revolution.* New York: 1967.

Peterson, H.L. *The Book of the Continental Soldier.* Harrisburg, Penna.: 1988.

Ray, Fred. *Frontier Forts and Battlefields.* ——: 1982.

Shumway, G. *Pennsylvania Longrifles of Note.* York, Penna.: 1968.

Shurlock, W.H., ed. *The Book of Buckskinning,* Vols. 1-4. Texarkana, Texas: 1980-1987.

Girty in Fiction

Note: The following selective list of books and films is included for the reader's interest only. With all due respect to the creators of the works, all contain historical inaccuracies in regard to Simon Girty.

—T.T.

Novels and Comics Narrative

Grey, Zane. *Betty Zane, The Last Trail, The Spirit of the Border.* New York: 1904-1912. (Reprinted with title changes by Tower Paperbacks in 1981.)

Pratt, Hugo. *Fort Wheeling, Billy James.* (Comics narratives printed throughout Europe and South America since 1967.)

Wright, Don. *The Captives.* New York: The Jameson Press, 1987.

Cinema and Television

Daniel Boone. (RKO-Radio Pictures; 1936).

Daniel Boone. (NBC-Television; September 24, 1964-August 27, 1970).

Daniel Boone through the Wilderness. (Sunset Pictures; 1926).

Daniel Boone, Trailblazer. (Republic Pictures; 1956).

Young Dan'l Boone. (CBS-Television; September 12, 1977-October 4, 1977).

"GIRTY·1774"

PART 1 —
BOOK OF GENESIS

*"The fathers have eaten sour grapes,
and the children's teeth are set on edge."*
— *Ezekiel, 18:2*

PROLOGUE ▬

SIMON GIRTY, SR., HAD NO CHOICE BUT TO LEAVE HIS NEW FARM AND RETURN TO THE CHAMBER'S MILL SETTLEMENT.

HE SOLD WHAT LITTLE HE HAD LEFT AND PAID THE FINE WHICH MAGISTRATE GEORGE CROGHAN AND THE CUMBERLAND COUNTY COURT HAD LEVELED AGAINST HIM.

NOT LONG AFTERWARDS, HE RESUMED HIS OLD CAREER AS A TRADER...

THE ELDER GIRTY FOUND A PARTNER, WITH WHOM HE SHARED BOTH BUSINESS EXPENSES AND HOME.

HIS NAME WAS JOHN TURNER.

TRADER GIRTY DEALT GOODS FOR FURS-- TOMAHAWKS FOR OTTER SKINS, SKINNING KNIVES AND SMOOTH- BORE MUSKETS FOR BEAR, POWDER AND BALL FOR BUFFALO, OR BITTER TRADE WHISKEY FOR FINE PELTS OF BEAVER OR MINK.

HIS CLIENTS COULD BE FOUND IN VILLAGES ALONG THE SUSQUEHANNA AND JUNIATA RIVERS OR ON HUNTING TRAILS IN THE ROLLING HILLS TO THE WEST.

THESE RED MEN WERE COMING TO DEPEND ON THE THINGS THAT MEN LIKE GIRTY BROUGHT THEM.

THE OLD MAN USUALLY TRAVELED ALONE, LEAVING HIS GROWING SONS-- THOMAS, SIMON, JAMES AND YOUNG GEORGE-- BEHIND WITH MARY TO TEND TO THE CABIN.

HE WOULD BE GONE FOR DAYS-- SOMETIMES WEEKS-- RETURNING LITTLE RICHER THAN HE'D BEEN WHEN HE'D DEPARTED.

MARY AND HER BOYS WOULD WAIT AT HOME. THERE WAS ALWAYS SOMETHING THERE TO KEEP THEM BUSY.

WEEKS LATER, GIRTY WOULD RETURN.

USUALLY, HE WOULD BRING FRIENDS.

IT WAS GOOD BUSINESS:...

...A JUG OF TRADE WHISKEY-- DILUTED WITH WATER, COLORED WITH A TWIST OR TWO OF TOBACCO, STUNG WITH A FEW HANDFULS OF PEPPER AND BLACK POWDER FOR TASTE. IT ONLY TOOK A FEW CUPS TO GET THE CUSTOMER IN THE FRAME OF MIND FOR PROPER BARGAINING.

HOWEVER, SUCH BUSINESS PRACTICES WERE PRONE TO CERTAIN RISKS...

ONE DIDN'T DEAL WITH THE DELAWARE LONG BEFORE REALIZING THAT THEY WERE A VERY *BRIGHT* PEOPLE. IT WAS A FIRE THAT WAS HARD TO PUT OUT-- EVEN WITH WATER AND ALCOHOL.

TO A DELAWARE LIKE NO-ME-THA-- "THE FISH"-- A MAN WAS NOT HIMSELF WHEN THE WHISKEY WENT FROM HIS *BELLY* TO HIS MIND...

AND NOT BEING HIMSELF HE COULD NOT BE HELD RESPON- SIBLE FOR WHAT MIGHT HAPPEN WHEN THE SPIRIT IN THE BOTTLE WAS WITHIN HIM.

B-BLAM!

IN SPRING, 1753, MARY GIRTY AND JOHN TURNER WERE WED.

ONE YEAR LATER THEY HAD A SON-- NAMED JOHN, AFTER HIS FATHER.

NOW THERE WERE SEVEN MOUTHS TO FEED...

THE SETTLERS AROUND CHAMBER'S MILL WERE QUICKLY USING UP THE GAME AND THE LAND. IT WAS TIME TO MOVE ELSEWHERE.

THE GREAT PENN FAMILY HAD PURCHASED NEW PROPERTY FROM THE INDIANS TO THE NORTHWEST. SETTLERS WERE AGAIN CUTTING WAGON ROADS BACK TO SHERMAN'S CREEK.

JOHN TURNER DECIDED THAT HIS NEW FAMILY WOULD JOIN THEM.

AND SO THEY BUILT A CABIN-- NEAR THE VERY GROUND WHERE THE GIRTY'S FORMER FARM HAD BEEN BURNED DOWN, FIVE YEARS BEFORE.

CHAPTER 2

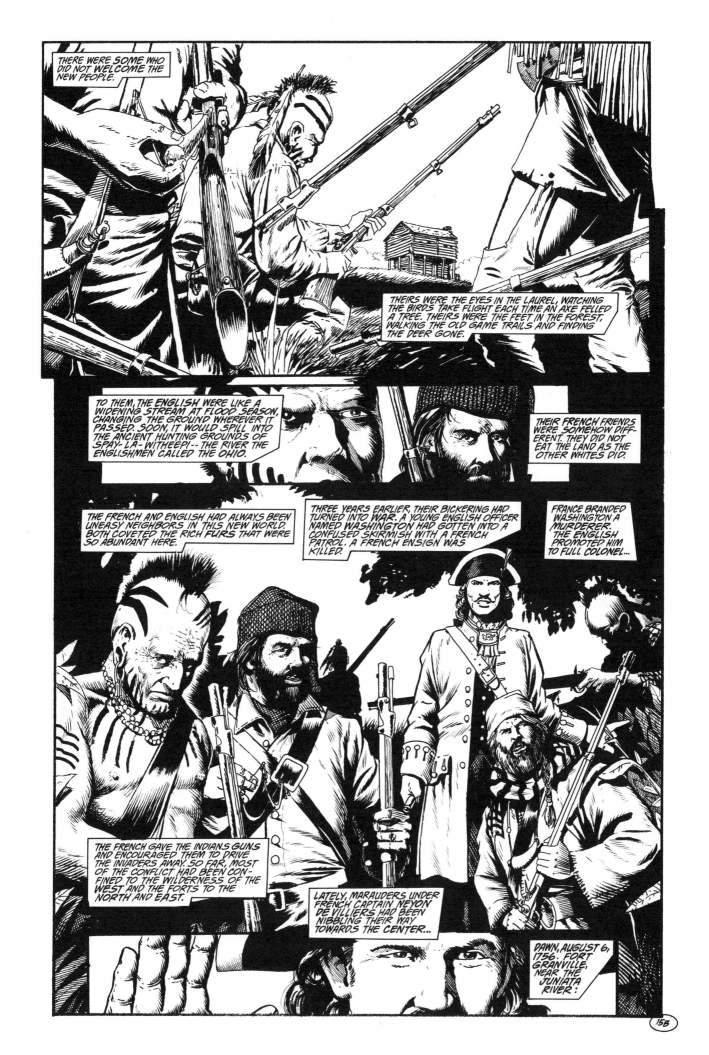

THERE WERE SOME WHO DID NOT WELCOME THE NEW PEOPLE.

THEIRS WERE THE EYES IN THE LAUREL, WATCHING THE BIRDS TAKE FLIGHT EACH TIME AN AXE FELLED A TREE. THEIRS WERE THE FEET IN THE FOREST, WALKING THE OLD GAME TRAILS AND FINDING THE DEER GONE.

TO THEM, THE ENGLISH WERE LIKE A WIDENING STREAM AT FLOOD SEASON, CHANGING THE GROUND WHEREVER IT PASSED. SOON, IT WOULD SPILL INTO THE ANCIENT HUNTING GROUNDS OF SPAY-LA-WITHEEPI -- THE RIVER THE ENGLISHMEN CALLED THE OHIO.

THEIR FRENCH FRIENDS WERE SOMEHOW DIFFERENT. THEY DID NOT EAT THE LAND AS THE OTHER WHITES DID.

THE FRENCH AND ENGLISH HAD ALWAYS BEEN UNEASY NEIGHBORS IN THIS NEW WORLD. BOTH COVETED THE RICH FURS THAT WERE SO ABUNDANT HERE.

THREE YEARS EARLIER, THEIR BICKERING HAD TURNED INTO WAR. A YOUNG ENGLISH OFFICER NAMED WASHINGTON HAD GOTTEN INTO A CONFUSED SKIRMISH WITH A FRENCH PATROL. A FRENCH ENSIGN WAS KILLED.

FRANCE BRANDED WASHINGTON A MURDERER. THE ENGLISH PROMOTED HIM TO FULL COLONEL...

THE FRENCH GAVE THE INDIANS GUNS AND ENCOURAGED THEM TO DRIVE THE INVADERS AWAY. SO FAR, MOST OF THE CONFLICT HAD BEEN CONFINED TO THE WILDERNESS OF THE WEST AND THE FORTS TO THE NORTH AND EAST.

LATELY, MARAUDERS UNDER FRENCH CAPTAIN NEYON DE VILLIERS HAD BEEN NIBBLING THEIR WAY TOWARDS THE CENTER...

DAWN, AUGUST 6, 1756: FORT GRANVILLE, NEAR THE JUNIATA RIVER:

15B

EVEN AS THE LITTLE STOCKADE BURNED AROUND THEM, THE DEFENDERS POURED FRANTIC VOLLEYS OF MUSKET FIRE AT THE ATTACKING FORCE.

BUT THE INDIAN SHARPSHOOTERS FOUND PROTECTION BEHIND THE BANKS OF JUNIATA CREEK.

AS THE LOGS OF THE STOCKADE BEGAN TO BURN AND GIVE WAY, THOSE INSIDE FIGHTING THE FIRE BECAME EASY TARGETS.

ARMSTRONG!!!

IT WAS ONLY A MATTER OF TIME...

SUDDENLY, THE FIRING STOPPED.

THE SETTLERS WERE HELPLESS, AND THE FRENCH COMMANDER KNEW IT.

HAILING THE STOCKADE, HE OFFERED QUARTER TO THOSE INSIDE IN RETURN FOR THEIR IMMEDIATE SURRENDER.

HOME FOR THE MUNCEY DELEWARES WAS 100 MILES AWAY...

... DEEP IN THE ROLLING MOUNTAINS TO THE WEST...

... BEYOND THE JUNIATA, ON THE ALLEGHENY.

ON THE FOURTH DAY, THEY STEPPED FROM THE ANCIENT TRAIL AND BEHELD A CITY...

... A PLACE CALLED KITTANNING!

THREE DAYS PASSED. THE PRISONERS HUDDLED FEARFULLY IN THE SHADOWS, CERTAIN THAT THEY WOULD SHARE JOHN TURNER'S FATE.

THEN, ON THE FOURTH MORNING, 16-YEAR-OLD SIMON WAS LED FROM THE LONGHOUSE...

BEFORE HIM, STANDING IN TWO ROWS THAT SEEMED TO STRETCH FOR AN INFINITY, WERE THE PEOPLE OF KITTANNING. THE ENTIRE VILLAGE HAD TURNED OUT FOR THE EVENT-- YOUNG AND OLD, MALE AND FEMALE, A SCREAMING MASS OF FOUL CAT-CALLS AND WAVING CLUBS.

THIS WAS THE GAUNTLET...

THE PAINTED MAN WHO HAD BROUGHT SIMON FROM THE LONGHOUSE NUDGED HIM FORWARD AND POINTED TO THE END OF THE LINE. THE BOY WAS TO RUN BETWEEN THE ROWS TOWARD THE MAIN COUNCIL HOUSE.

IF HE FALTERED, HE WOULD DIE. IF HE FELL, HE WOULD BE FORCED TO HIS FEET TO TRY AGAIN.

THERE WAS NOTHING LEFT TO DO...

... BUT RUN...

... RUN...

...RUN...

.... RUN... ....

HE OPENED HIS EYES TO THE SCENT OF EARTH AND BARK, SWEET CORN AND WOODSMOKE, WOOL BLANKETS AND FRESHLY-STRETCHED DEER HIDE.

SIMON HADN'T EXPECTED DEATH TO SMELL QUITE LIKE THIS...

NOR HAD HE EXPECTED HIS BRUISED LIMBS AND BROKEN BONES TO STILL HURT...

HE HAD EXPECTED TO SEE ANGELS.

YES... SEEING ANGELS WAS ALL RIGHT...

SHE TOUCHED HIM GENTLY, APPLYING A COOL, SWEET-SMELLING OINTMENT OF WHITE OAK TEA TO HIS WOUNDS...

...STROKING HIM TENDERLY... CAREFULLY... JUST LIKE MOTHER USED TO, WHEN SIMON WAS ILL...

... AND AS SHE TOUCHED HIM, SHE WHISPERED.

"...YOU RAN WELL, YOUNG ONE. YOU WERE BRAVE.... STRONG... SO NOW YOU WILL BE ONE OF US. WE ARE YOUR FAMILY. I AM YOUR MOTHER...

"...WE WILL CARE FOR YOU. WE WILL LOVE YOU...

..."YOU WILL LIVE WITH US, AND NONE SHALL HARM YOU...

"NEVER AGAIN WILL ONE OF OUR PEOPLE RAISE A HAND AGAINST YOU."

23B

HER WORDS WERE TRUE. SIMON WAS NEVER BEATEN AGAIN—FOR THESE PEOPLE NEVER STRUCK THEIR CHILDREN. NOR WAS HE EVER HUNGRY, AS HE HAD OFTEN BEEN WITH HIS WHITE FAMILY. FOR THESE PEOPLE SHARED WHAT THEY HAD WITH ALL.

TO THEIR LOVED ONES THEY SHOWED KINDNESS AND GENEROSITY. FOR THEIR ENEMIES THEY RESERVED ONLY HORRIBLE SUFFERING AND TERROR.

ALAS, THE ENGLISHMEN DID NOT SCARE EASILY. ONE MONTH AFTER THE FALL OF FORT GRANVILLE, THE WHITE ARMY BURNED KITTANNING TO THE GROUND. MANY ENGLISH CAPTIVES WERE FREED—AMONG THEM THE ELDEST GIRTY BROTHER, THOMAS.

THE FLEEING DELAWARE PREPARED THEMSELVES FOR THE TROUBLES AHEAD. A WHITE WOMAN WAS TORTURED IN OFFERING TO THE WAR SPIRIT. THE REMAINING CAPTIVES WERE DIVIDED AMONG THE TRIBES WHO HAD ASSISTED IN THE EASTERN RAIDS.

THE DELAWARES KEPT MARY TURNER AND HER YOUNGEST SONS GEORGE AND JOHN. THE SHAWNEES CLAIMED 14-YEAR-OLD JAMES.

SIMON WAS SENT FAR AWAY—TO NEW YORK, WITH CHIEF KAYINGWAURTO'S SENECAS.

THE SENECAS TAUGHT HIM THEIR WAYS. IN THE GLOW OF THEIR COUNCIL FIRES HE LISTENED TO THE ANCIENT STORIES AND FINE SPEECHES OF THE FATHERS. FOR THIS WAS HOW THE HISTORY OF THE SENECAS WAS KEPT ALIVE.

LONG AGO, THEY'D DEVELOPED A GIFT FOR HEARING AND REMEMBERING WORDS. IT WAS SOON DISCOVERED THAT SIMON, TOO, SHARED THIS GIFT.

HE LEARNED THEIR LANGUAGE SWIFTLY. HE STUDIED THE ELDERS AS THEY SPOKE, FASCINATED BY THE SUBTLETIES OF THEIR WORDS AND MOVEMENTS.

SIMON GIRTY LIVED WITH THE SENECAS FOR NEARLY FOUR YEARS...

...DEEP WITHIN THE WILDERNESS...

24B

WINTER,
1759--
FORT PITT:

PART 2 —
PITTSBURGH

*"He was the bravest-looking man I ever saw.
He could speak more Indian languages than
any man I ever heard of. He was very friendly
and kind to all Americans whom he had known
or previously met with.*

*". . . Girty and I pledged ourselves
one to another, hand in hand, for life
and death, when there was nobody
in the wilderness but God and us."*

— *Simon Kenton*

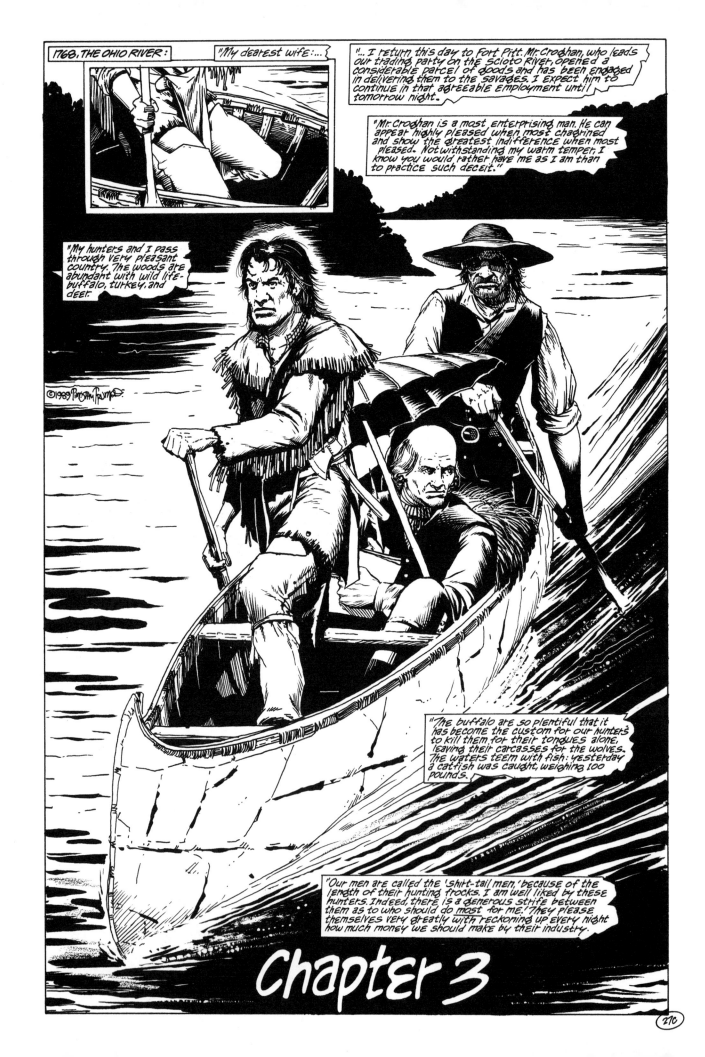

1768, THE OHIO RIVER:

"My dearest wife:..."

"...I return this day to Fort Pitt. Mr. Croghan, who leads our trading party on the Scioto River, opened a considerable parcel of goods and has been engaged in delivering them to the savages. I expect him to continue in that agreeable employment until tomorrow night.

"Mr. Croghan is a most enterprising man. He can appear highly pleased when most chagrined and show the greatest indifference when most pleased. Notwithstanding my warm temper, I know you would rather have me as I am than to practice such deceit."

"My hunters and I pass through very pleasant country. The woods are abundant with wild life—buffalo, turkey, and deer.

©1989 Timothy Truman.

"The buffalo are so plentiful that it has become the custom for our hunters to kill them for their tongues alone, leaving their carcasses for the wolves. The waters teem with fish: yesterday a catfish was caught, weighing 100 pounds.

"Our men are called the 'shirt-tail men,' because of the length of their hunting frocks. I am well liked by these hunters. Indeed, there is a generous strife between them as to who should do most for me! They please themselves very greatly with reckoning up every night how much money we should make by their industry.

CHAPTER 3

"Chief among those seeking my favor is Simon Girty. Indeed, Girty is particularly attached to me."

"Girty is pleasant, good natured, jovial, and honest to a fault. It is said that he once sold his only horse so that he might repay a debt, and then walked several hundred miles to deliver the money."

"Simon Girty is highly praised by his fellow hunters. He is an incredible marksman--though perhaps not as good as Stoner or Diverbaugh. He was captive of the savages for some time, and learned much woods-craft from them."

"Because Girty is proficient in many of the tribal languages, Mr. Croghan and I frequently use him as an interpreter."

"...I now approach Fort Pitt with Girty and another man, and hope to see you in Philadelphia soon. I remain, my dear, your most humble and obedient servant..."

Geo. Morgan

"He is so well liked by the savages that one of their chiefs, Katepocomen, has adopted the name 'Simon Girty.' This is said to be the greatest honor an Indian can pay another man."

"Even the Shawanese, who are so often ill-disposed towards us, seem to think highly of Girty."

IN THE YEARS SINCE HIS RELEASE, SIMON GIRTY HAD FREQUENTLY BEEN ENLISTED BY FORT PITT'S ROUGH, INDEPENDENT TRADERS TO INTERPRET FOR THEIR INDIAN CLIENTS. BUT SIMON'S GREATEST TALENTS BECAME TRULY EVIDENT AFTER HE JOINED GEORGE MORGAN'S TRADING EMPIRE.

IT DIDN'T SEEM TO MATTER THAT THE JOB OFTEN BROUGHT HIM INTO CONTACT WITH GEORGE CROGHAN, THE MAN WHO HAD BURNED HIS FATHER'S FARM. THERE WERE FEW BOSSES IN THE LANDS WHERE SIMON GIRTY WAS PAID TO ROAM.

GIRTY'S FORAYS WITH MORGAN'S LONGHUNTERS TOOK HIM DEEP INTO THE COUNTRY THAT THE TRIBES CALLED KAN-TU-KEE. HE WAS AMONG THE FIRST WHITE MEN TO EVER SEE THAT GAME-FILLED WILDERNESS AND COAX THE INDIANS WHO HUNTED THERE INTO MORGAN'S TRADING CAMPS.

FOR THE FIRST TIME SINCE HE'D LEFT THE SENECAS, SIMON GIRTY FELT USEFUL. HE FELT NEEDED...

SIMON'S FAMILY HAD ALSO DECIDED TO STAY NEAR THE FORT. GEORGE WAS ONLY 14 WHEN HE'D LEFT THE DELAWARES. SINCE THEN, HE'D SPENT MUCH OF HIS TIME VISITING AND TRADING WITH OLD FRIENDS IN NEARBY DELAWARE HUNTING CAMPS.

JAMES, TWO YEARS OLDER THAN GEORGE, WAS A MISCHIEVOUS RASCAL. HIS LAST EMPLOYER WAS A GULLIBLE LINGUIST, SEARCHING FOR A LEGENDARY RACE OF WELSH-SPEAKING INDIANS. JAMES CONFIRMED THAT THE TRIBE DID, INDEED, EXIST AND--OVER A FEW BOTTLES OF VERY EXPENSIVE BRANDY-HELPED THE MAN COMPILE A VOCABULARY OF THEIR LANGUAGE...

THOMAS, THE OLDEST, HAD BEEN AT FORT PITT SINCE COLONEL ARMSTRONG HAD FREED HIM AT KITTANNING. HE'D BECOME A HARD-WORKING LABORER, PACKING GOODS ABOARD WILDERNESS-BOUND TRADING BATTEAUS.

JOHN TURNER, JR. WAS 5 WHEN HE AND HIS MOTHER WERE RELEASED. NOW BARELY INTO HIS TEENS, HE WAS THE ONLY ONE OF THE BOYS WHO'D BEEN BAPTISED.

SIMON'S CLOSEST FRIEND AT PITT WAS ALEXANDER MC KEE, A WEALTHY, HALF-BREED TRADER WHOSE FATHER HAD KNOWN THE GIRTYS BACK AT CHAMBER'S MILL. MC KEE WAS ALWAYS GOOD FOR A DRINK IN RETURN FOR ANY TRIBAL GOSSIP THAT SIMON COULD BRING HIM.

FOR A WHILE, SIMON HAD STAYED WITH HIS MOTHER AND BROTHERS IN SQUIRREL HILL. LATELY, HE'D TAKEN A ROOM AT THE HOME OF WILLIAM CRAWFORD, AN UP-AND-COMING LAND AGENT WHO KEPT GIRTY ABREAST OF THE NEWS FROM THE EAST.

BESIDES, CRAWFORD HAD A VERY PRETTY DAUGHTER...

ON THE DARK RIDGES OVERLOOKING THE FORT, THE EYES OF THE FOREST WATCHED AS THE MUDDY LITTLE SETTLEMENT CONTINUED TO GROW...

THEY HAD BEEN HERE WHEN THE FRENCH FIRST BUILT THE FORT AND CALLED IT FORT DUQUESNE.

THEY REMEMBERED THE DAY THEY HAD HELPED THE FRENCHMEN DEFEND ITS WALLS AGAINST GENERAL BRADDOCK'S MIGHTY ARMY. ON THAT DAY, THE ENGLISH GENERAL HAD DIED, AND THE TRIBES HAD TAKEN ALMOST 1,000 BRITISH SCALPS FROM THE BLOODY FIELD.

BUT THE WONDROUS VICTORY HAD BEEN HOLLOW. FOR ONLY A FEW YEARS LATER, THE FRENCH FLED WITHOUT A FIGHT, LEAVING THE FORT TO THE RED-COATS.

THE BRITISH HAD NAMED THE FORT PITT, IN HONOR OF ONE OF THEIR FAT FATHERS, AND PROMISED THE PEOPLE FRIENDSHIP, TOBACCO, GUNS, AND RUM.

THE GIFTS DID NOT COME. A GREAT CHIEF NAMED PONTIAC RALLIED THE TRIBES OF ALL THE FOREST NATIONS. FOR MONTHS THEY RAZED ENGLISH FORTS TO THE WEST. BUT FORT PITT WOULD NOT FALL...

AT LAST THE ENGLISH SENT GIFTS TO THE LONGHOUSES OF THE DELAWARE AND SHAWNEE -- BLANKETS THAT CRAWLED WITH THE SPOTTED SICKNESS CALLED SMALLPOX! EVEN AS THEIR WOMEN AND CHILDREN DIED, THE INDIANS WERE DEFEATED BY THE BRITISH AT A PLACE CALLED BUSHY RUN.

SINCE THAT DAY, THERE HAD BEEN PEACE...

...PEACE-- AS LONG AS YOU IGNORED THE ONCE-PROUD WARRIORS LAYING SENSELESS IN THEIR HOMES, STINKING OF ENGLISH RUM...

...PEACE--IF YOU DID NOT COUNT THE BODIES OF DEAD SHAWNEE HUNTERS ON THE RIVERBANK, SHOT FOR SPORT BY PASSING WHITE BOATSMEN...

...PEACE--IF YOU DIDN'T PAY HEED TO STOLEN HORSES AND WHITE SCALPS THAT THE YOUNG MEN OCCASIONALLY BROUGHT HOME AS PROOF OF THEIR MANHOOD...

IT WAS CLEAR THAT VERY SOON THE ENTIRE WORLD WAS GOING TO CHANGE...

©1989 TIMOTHY TRUMAN 4

1774

SAMUEL SEMPLE'S TAVERN:

THE DREAM OF EVERY FRONTIERSMAN IN PITTSBURGH WAS TO ONE DAY HAVE LAND OF HIS OWN. SUCH LAND COULD ONLY BE FOUND WEST-- BEYOND THE OHIO-- IN THE COUNTRY CLAIMED BY THE SHAWNEES.

HOWEVER, CERTAIN GENTLEMEN FROM VIRGINIA ALSO CLAIMED THAT LAND, BY VIRTUE OF A HANDFUL OF PAPERS THEY HAD COLLECTED FROM THE INDIANS AFTER THE LATE WARS. SOMEDAY, THIS LAND WOULD BE SOLD TO THE FRONTIERSMEN, AND GREAT FORTUNES WOULD BE MADE.

IT WAS A GOOD PLAN-- AS LONG AS PITTSBURGH REMAINED UNDER THE JURISDICTION OF VIRGINIA.

THEN, ONE DAY, THE MAP CHANGED. THE COLONY OF PENNSYLVANIA WAS GRANTED A NEW COUNTY. ON THE FRINGES OF THAT COUNTY WAS A MUDDY LITTLE TOWN CALLED PITTSBURGH...

SUDDENLY, THE FRONTIERSMEN OF FORT PITT WERE PENNSYLVANIANS. AND PENNSYLVANIANS COULD NO LONGER FILE FOR LAND OWNED BY GENTLEMEN FROM VIRGINIA...

SIMON GIRTY ENTERED THE WORLD OF POLITICS...

THERE WERE SOME WHO THOUGHT THAT MEN LIKE GIRTY COULD PROVE VERY USEFUL.

HE HAD MANY FRIENDS AMONG THESE LAND-HUNGRY PEASANTS. IF THE BORDER RUFFIANS WERE KEPT ANGRY ENOUGH, THE NEW BOUNDRIES MIGHT BE RECONSIDERED. THE VIRGINIANS WOULD FILL THEIR LANDS AND THEIR PURSES...

...AND MEN LIKE GIRTY WOULD FILL IMPORTANT NEW POSTS, NEGOTIATING WITH THE INDIANS.

DR. JOHN CONNOLLY AND THE PEOPLE HE SERVED THOUGHT IT WAS A WONDERFUL IDEA.

RIOTS BETWEEN THE PENNSYLVANIA AND VIRGINIA FACTIONS RAGED ALMOST DAILY. MEN ON BOTH SIDES WERE ARRESTED ON CHARGES RANGING FROM ASSAULT TO SLANDER.

AT THE HEIGHT OF THE TROUBLES, A PARTISAN WAS APPREHENDED BY THE PENNSYLVANIANS AND DETAINED IN THE HOUSE OF AENEAS MACKAY.

GIRTY'S VIRGINIANS BURST INTO MACKAY'S HOME TO FREE THEIR COMRADE. AS THE SHARP-TONGUED MRS. MACKAY LEVELED A BARRAGE OF UNLADY-LIKE INSULTS AT THE MOB, GEORGE ASTON TOOK A DRUKEN SWIPE AT HER WITH HIS CUTLASS.

GIRTY WARDED THE BLOW AWAY WITH HIS OWN ARM...

UNTIL THE BORDER DISPUTE COULD BE SETTLED, THERE WERE *TWO* GOVERNMENTS IN PITTSBURGH. NEITHER RECOGNIZED THE AUTHORITY OF THE OTHER.

DR. CONNOLLY WAS MADE CAPTAIN OF THE MILITIA BY HIS ARCH-PATRON IN VIRGINIA, *LORD DUNMORE*, AND HUMBLY ASSUMED LEADERSHIP OF THE VIRGINIA FACTION. CONNOLLY RE-CHRISTENED THE OUTPOST "FORT DUNMORE," AND MADE SURE THAT SAMUEL SEMPLE'S KEGS WERE ALWAYS KEPT FULL FOR THE REGULAR MEETINGS OF THE MILITIA.

WHATEVER DUNMORE AND CONNOLLY WERE PLANNING WAS FINE WITH SIMON GIRTY. HE HAD NO INTEREST IN THE LANDS BEYOND THE OHIO THAT WERE BEING PROMISED TO THE OTHERS.

ALL THAT COUNTED WAS THAT HE WAS AMONG FRIENDS AND THAT HE WAS RESPECTED. MEN LIKE JOHN CONNOLLY AND GEORGE MORGAN HAD GIVEN HIS LIFE A PURPOSE...

...AND IF THERE WAS AN OPEN KEG IN THE BARGAIN, WELL...

...SO MUCH THE BETTER...

GOT ANYONE TO GO *HOME* TO, FRIEND?

H-HAD A LIL' HALFBREED GAL, 'WHILE BACK, BUT I RECKON SHE DIDN'T LIKE MY *HABITS*...

WHO MIGHT YOU BE, TALL MAN?

NAME'S *SIMON BUTLER*-- LATE OF THE BIG SANDY.

I'VE HEARD OF YOU, BUTLER. YOU RUN WITH *GREATHOUSE* AND HIS BUNCH. WHAT'S OL' JAKE UP TO THESE DAYS...?

WHATEVER IT IS, IT SURE AIN'T THE *LORD'S* WORK. GREATHOUSE AND I PARTED WAYS SOME MONTHS BACK, AND I CAN'T SAY I *MISS* HIM...

"...NOW WHAT SAY WE GET YOU *HOME*, FRIEND?"

JACOB GREATHOUSE HAD INDEED BEEN UP TO NO GOOD...

APRIL 30, 1774. A SMALL ISLAND IN THE OHIO RIVER, NEAR THE MOUTH OF YELLOW CREEK:

CHIEF LOGAN OF THE MINGO TRIBE HAD ALWAYS BEEN A PEACEFUL MAN...

WHEN HIS SHAWNEE BROTHERS HAD ASKED HIM TO JOIN THEM IN WAR AGAINST THE WHITES, LOGAN-- TAL-GA-YEE--TA-- HAD ALWAYS COUNCILED FOR PEACE...

NOW, HIS BROTHER... HIS SISTER... HER UNBORN CHILD... HER HUSBAND... HIS KINSMEN...

...ALL WERE DEAD, AND HIS LITTLE COUSIN STOLEN...

...NEVER HAD LOGAN RAISED HIS HAND AGAINST A WHITE MAN...

33c

"NO MORE!"

"FOR EACH OF MY FAMILY WHO HAS DIED, THREE WHITES WILL DIE! FOR EVERY DROP OF BLOOD THAT HAS BEEN SPILLED, I SHALL BRING THEM BLOOD IN BUCKETS!"

"I SHALL BURN AWAY MY GRIEF WITH THE FLAMES OF WAR!"

WHAT DID YOU KILL MY PEOPLE ON YELLOW CREEK FOR? THE WHITE PEOPLE KILLED MY KIN ON THE CONESTOGA A GREAT WHILE AGO, AND I THOUGHT NOTHING OF THAT. BUT YOU KILLED MY KIN ON YELLOW CREEK, AND TOOK MY COUSIN PRISONER. THEN I THOUGHT I MUST KILL TOO, AND I HAVE BEEN THREE TIMES AT WAR SINCE. THE INDIANS ARE NOT ANGRY—ONLY MYSELF.

—CAPT. JOHN LOGAN
JULY 21, 1774

FOR MONTHS, SHAWNEE WAR PARTIES HAD BEEN KILLING ANY WHITE HUNTER WHO TRESPASSED ONTO THEIR LAND. IT BECAME CLEAR THAT THE COUNTRY BEYOND THE OHIO WOULD NEVER BE SETTLED WITHOUT AN INDIAN WAR.

BEFORE THE YELLOW CREEK MASSACRE, LOGAN THE MINGO AND OLD CHIEF CORNSTALK OF THE SHAWNEE HAD KEPT THEIR WARRIORS FROM ATTACKING WHITE SETTLEMENTS EAST OF THE OHIO. BUT NOW LOGAN'S FAMILY WAS DEAD. THE VIRGINIA LAND BARONS HAD THEIR WAR.

DR. JOHN CONNOLLY HAD SERVED HIS MASTERS WELL...

LORD JOHN MURRAY--THE EARL OF DUNMORE--HAD RECENTLY ARRIVED IN PENNSYLVANIA TO OVERSEE CONNOLLY'S SCHEMES. THE GOOD DOCTOR HAD RENAMED THE LITTLE FORT IN DUNMORE'S HONOR. NOW A SPLENDID LITTLE "ADVENTURE" WOULD ALSO BEAR HIS NAME.

DUNMORE, HIMSELF, WOULD LEAD AN ARMY OF 1400 MEN FROM PENNSYLVANIA. COLONEL ANDREW LEWIS WOULD BRING ANOTHER 1200 MILITIAMEN NORTHWARD FROM VIRGINIA. CAUGHT BETWEEN THE TWO FORCES, THE MARAUDING LOGAN AND HIS SHAWNEE ALLIES WOULD BE SUBDUED.

THE BEST WOODSMEN WERE RECRUITED TO ACT AS SCOUTS AND MESSENGERS FOR THE ARMIES. SIMON GIRTY WAS AMONG THE FIRST TO BE ENLISTED. AND WITH HIM CAME SIMON BUTLER...

TO THE PEOPLE OF THE FRONTIER, YOUNG BUTLER WAS QUICKLY BECOMING A LEGEND.

FEW WHITE MEN HAD DARED TO VENTURE INTO THE FORBIDDEN SHAWNEE HUNTING GROUNDS OF THE GREAT KANAWHA RIVER. BUT BUTLER ALREADY KNEW THE COUNTRY WELL...

THE BIG WOODSMAN WAS RUNNING FROM HIS PAST. AS A BOY, HE'D KILLED A MAN IN VIRGINIA. SINCE THEN, HE'D SPENT HIS LIFE SEEKING THE SECRET PATHWAYS OF THE FOREST. IN THE WILDERNESS, HIS SOUL HAD FOUND PEACE...

... AND IN THAT SOUL, SIMON GIRTY FOUND KINSHIP.

SOMEDAY, THE WORLD WOULD CALL BUTLER BY HIS REAL NAME-- SIMON KENTON.

SIMON GIRTY WOULD ALWAYS CALL HIM FRIEND...

FROM THE KANAWHA, THE TWO COMPANIONS VEERED SOUTHEAST THROUGH THE SHA-DOWED VALLEYS OF THE GAULEY RIVER. AT RICH CREEK, THEY TOOK A SHORT-CUT OVER THE GREAT GAULEY MOUNTAIN, MARKING A PATH THAT WOULD HELP LEWIS' VIRGINIANS AVOID THE SHAWNEE WAR TRAILS OF THE LOWER NEW RIVER.

THESE WERE GOOD DAYS, FILLED WITH ADVENTURE AND PURPOSE. TIME AND AGAIN THEY CROSSED THE VAST WILDERNESS THAT SEPARATED THE TWO ARMIES. EVERYTHING WAS GOING AS PLANNED. THEN, JUST AS LEWIS' WEARY VIRGINIANS NEARED THE APPOINTED MEETING PLACE ON THE OHIO, LORD DUNMORE SENT A NEW MESSAGE...

GIRTY, KENTON, AND A FELLOW SCOUT LEFT THE ORDERS IN A HOLLOW TREE, NEAR THE PLACE CALLED POINT PLEASANT.

DUNMORE HAD CHANGED HIS MIND, IT SEEMED...

INSTEAD OF MEETING THE PENNSYLVANIANS AT THE POINT, AS ORIGINALLY PLANNED, LEWIS WAS TO BRING HIS VIRGINIANS FARTHER NORTH--TO DUNMORE'S CAMP ON THE HOCKHOCKING.

COLONEL LEWIS REFUSED.

HIS MEN WERE TIRED AND STARVING. DUNMORE HAD PROVISIONS THAT THE VIRGINIANS BADLY NEEDED.

NO...

...LEWIS WOULD MOVE TO POINT PLEASANT, AND REST HIS MEN THERE! LET DUNMORE COME TO HIM!

HIS LORDSHIP WAS NOT AMUSED.

AGAIN, HE SENT OUT SCOUTS, ORDERING LEWIS TO BREAK CAMP HEAD FOR THE INDIAN TOWN. LORD DUNMORE WOULD JOIN THEM EN ROUTE, AND TOGETHER THEY WOULD STRIKE AT THE MAIN SHAWNEE STRONGHOLDS.

AGAIN, LEWIS REFUSED.

THE GRUELING TRIP HAD TAKEN ITS TOLL. HIS ARMY COULD GO NO FARTHER WITHOUT REST AND FOOD.

THESE MEN HAD LEFT THEIR HOMES AND FAMILIES TO FIGHT THE SHAWNEE...

...NOW THEY WERE BEING FORSAKEN.

IT WOULD BE SUICIDAL FOR LEWIS TO MARCH NOW. IF DUNMORE SENT SUPPLIES AND MOVED HIS ARMY CLOSER, THE VIRGINIANS WOULD CONSIDER JOINING THE ASSAULT.

OTHERWISE, HIS LORDSHIP WOULD JUST HAVE TO WAIT UNTIL THE VIRGINIANS WERE WELL AGAIN.

LORD JOHN MURRAY, EARL OF DUNMORE, DID NOT SEEM OVERLY ANXIOUS TO MEET COLONEL LEWIS AT POINT PLEASANT.

HE WAS READY TO MARCH AGAINST THE SHAWNEE, AND MARCH HE WOULD.

INTOXICATED BY THE EXCITEMENT OF IT ALL, LORD DUNMORE FOUND CAUSE TO CELEBRATE.

A DANCE MR. GIRTY...

HIS LORDSHIP HAD LEARNED THAT CERTAIN OF HIS SCOUTS HAD ONCE BEEN CAPTIVES OF THE INDIANS. FOR HIS DIVERSION, HE DESIRED TO SEEN AN INDIAN DANCE.

STRIPPED TO THE WAIST, GIRTY AND HIS HALF-BROTHER JOHN TURNER JOINED TWO OTHER SCOUTS AROUND THE BONFIRE...

SOON, THE CAMP WAS AN RINGING IN AN UPROAR OF PRIMAL YELLS AND WILD SCREAMS. THE SOLDIERS HOWLED WITH GLEE, POUNDING THEIR FISTS INTO THEIR RIFLE STOCKS TO CREATE A DRUM BEAT.

THE DANCERS PRANCED AND STRUTTED, KICKING LOGS INTO THE AIR, SENDING CASCADES OF SPARKS IN EVERY DIRECTION.

DEEP WITHIN THE FOREST, SIMON GIRTY DANCED A SENECA DANCE OF LIFE AND WAR...

... FOR WERE THE SHAWNEES NOT THE ANCIENT ENEMIES OF THE NORTHERN SENECAS? HAD NOT THE MINGOES ONCE BEEN SENECAS THEMSELVES, BUT DENIED THEIR BROTHERS TO CREATE THEIR OWN TRIBE?

IN THE MORNING, DUNMORE'S FORCE RESUMED THEIR MARCH AGAINST THE SHAWNEE TOWNS.

BUT WHEN THEY ARRIVED THERE, THEY FOUND THE VILLAGES NEARLY EMPTY...

37C

DAWN, OCTOBER 10,1774. COLONEL ANDREW LEWIS' ENCAMPMENT AT POINT PLEASANT:

1,000 WARRIORS STREAMED OUT OF THE WOODS AGAINST LEWIS' STARVING VIRGINIANS.

THE BATTLE RAGED DEEP INTO THE EVENING. 75 OF THE WHITE SOLDIERS DIED. 100 MORE LAY WOUNDED.

THEN, AS SUDDENLY AS THEY HAD APPEARED, THE INDIANS RETREATED INTO THE FOREST.

INCREDIBLY, THE BATTERED VIRGINIANS HAD WON.

COL. LEWIS HAD LOST HIS BROTHER AND MOST OF HIS OFFICERS. THERE WAS NO MEDICINE FOR THE WOUNDED. PROVISIONS WERE GONE...

LORD DUNMORE HAD 170 CATTLE, 25 TONS OF FLOUR, AND RESTED TROOPS. YET HE ORDERED LEWIS'S SHATTERED MEN TO CROSS THE OHIO AND JOIN HIS MARCH ON THE SHAWNEE TOWNS...

DAYS LATER, THE TWO ARMIES FINALLY MET...

THE VIRGINIANS WERE ON THE VERGE OF MUTINY. RATHER THAN RISKING OPEN WARFARE WITH HIS OWN COMMANDING OFFICER, THE PROUD COL. LEWIS WITHDREW HIS TROOPS BACK TO POINT PLEASANT.

THE VIRGINIA MILITIA HAD WON A MIRACULOUS VICTORY AGAINST THE ENEMY. NOT TO BE OUTDONE, HIS LORDSHIP SET HIS SIGHTS ON THE SHAWNEE CAPITAL OF CHILLICOTHE.

HOWEVER, 15 MILES FROM THEIR TARGET, A STRANGE APPARITION APPEARED...

HEY! HOLD YOUR FIRE, LADDIES! I'M COMIN' OUT!

CORNSTALK AND HIS CHIEFS WISH A WORD WITH YE! YE CARRY THE WAR TO THEIR HOME, AND THEY FEAR FOR THEIR LOVIN' FAMILIES!

COME! THEY WISH TO SPEAK PEACE!

HIS NAME WAS MATTHEW ELLIOTT...

HE WAS AN INDEPENDANT TRAPPER WHO DEALT WITH THE SHAWNEE...AN IRISHMAN, LIKE GIRTY'S FATHER...

DESTINY WOULD LINK THE FATE OF SIMON GIRTY TO THAT OF THIS STRANGE LITTLE MAN...

THUS, THE FOREST PEOPLE ENTERED A PERIOD OF RELUCTANT PEACE WITH THE WHITE MEN...

NEVER AGAIN WOULD THE LONG KNIVES MARCH AGAINST THE OHIO TRIBES...AS LONG AS THE WHITES COULD SETTLE THE HUNTING GROUNDS CALLED KAN-TU-KEE.

OLD CORNSTALK...WHITE EYES...THE GRENADIER SQUAW...ALL THE PRINCIPAL CHIEFS AGREED TO HONOR THE TREATY...

...EVERYONE, THAT IS, BUT MINGO LOGAN...

OCTOBER 26, 1774 AT LOGAN'S CAMP ON CONGO CREEK:

A SENTRY SAW GIRTY GO ALONE TO MEET WITH THE MINGO CHIEF. IT WASN'T A MEETING THAT GIRTY WAS LOOKING FORWARD TO. IT WAS SAID THAT LOGAN WAS IN A FOUL MOOD.

THE SCOUT'S FEARS PROVED TO BE GROUND-LESS.

CAPTAIN JOHN LOGAN--TAL-GA-YEE-TA OF THE MINGO--WAS A VERY CIVILIZED MAN--

< AH! GIR-TEE! COME...SIT WITH ME. REMEMBER MY WORDS, AND CARRY THEM BACK TO YOUR PEOPLE.>

CHAPTER 4

< IS THERE ANY WHITE MAN WHO COULD SAY THAT HE EVER ENTERED LOGAN'S HOUSE HUNGRY, AND I DID NOT GIVE HIM MEAT? OR CAME COLD AND NAKED, AND I DID NOT GIVE HIM CLOTHES?>

< IN PAST WARS WITH THE WHITES, I REMAINED IDLE IN MY CABIN, AND COUNSELED FOR PEACE. MY BROTHERS WOULD PASS BY POINTING AND SAYING: 'THERE IS LOGAN, FRIEND OF WHITE MAN!' INDEED, I ONCE THOUGHT OF COMING TO YOUR TOWNS, TO LIVE AMONG YOU.>

< THEN, LAST SPRING, THE WHITE MEN CAME AND MURDERED MY FAMILY, UN-PROVOKED AND IN COLD BLOOD, SPARING NOT EVEN MY WOMEN AND CHILDREN! THERE RUNS NOT A DROP OF MY BLOOD IN THE VEINS OF ANY LIVING CREATURE!>

THIS CALLED ON ME FOR MY REVENGE! I HAVE SOUGHT IT! I HAVE KILLED MANY WHITE MEN-- BUT NOW I HAVE FULLY GLUTTED MY VENGEANCE!

< NOW, YOU SAY THERE IS PEACE IN MY COUNTRY, AND I REJOICE. BUT DO NOT MISTAKE MY JOY FOR FEAR-- I HAVE NEVER FELT FEAR. I WILL NEVER TURN ON MY HEEL TO SAVE MY OWN LIFE!>

< I ASK YOU, MY FRIEND: WHO IS THERE TO MOURN FOR LOGAN WHEN HE DIES...?>

"<...NO ONE.>"

© 1989

40 D

THE SCOUT CARRIED THE SPEECH TO DUNMORE.

GIRTY HAD NEVER LEARNED TO READ OR WRITE, SO HE DICTATED THE SPEECH TO MILITIAMAN JOHN GIBSON. ALTHOUGH GIBSON HAD ONCE LIVED WITH ONE OF LOGAN'S DAUGHTERS AND THUS KNEW THE CHIEF WELL, THE SENTRY DID NOT SEE HIM GO WITH GIRTY.

GIBSON READ THE SPEECH. THE MEN WERE VISIBLY MOVED.

THE MISTY-EYED DUNMORE COMMENDED GIBSON FOR HIS IMPASSIONED RECITATION.

HOWEVER, HIS LORDSHIP'S SYMPATHY FOR LOGAN'S GRIEF DID NOT LAST LONG...

HE SENT GIRTY'S OLD LANDLORD, WILLIAM CRAWFORD, TO "PUNISH" THE MINGOES FOR NOT SIGNING THE TREATY.

THE GREAT CHIEF WAS NOT AMONG THOSE SLAIN...

DUNMORE'S SPLENDID LITTLE ADVENTURE WAS FINISHED. THE MILITIAMEN RETURNED HOME...

...AND SIMON GIRTY AND THE MAN KNOWN AS SIMON BUTLER PARTED WAYS.

IN THE CANE-LANDS, IT WAS SAID, THERE WAS GAME A-PLENTY AND GROUND WAITING FOR THE CLEARING. IT WAS A PLACE WHERE A MAN COULD FIND HIMSELF.

THE NEXT TIME THEY MET, THE FORTUNES OF BOTH MEN WOULD BE VERY CHANGED, INDEED...

BUTLER WAS BOUND ONCE AGAIN FOR THE BIG SANDY, DETERMINED TO DISCOVER THE FABLED REGION CALLED THE CANE-LANDS.

SIMON BUTLER-- SIMON KENTON-- WAS CERTAIN THAT HIS DESTINY WOULD BE FORGED THERE.

GIRTY'S EFFORTS DURING THE WAR HAD NOT ESCAPED NOTICE...

AS HIS REPUTATION AS AN INTERPRETER AND SCOUT INCREASED, HE WAS SENT ON DANGEROUS DIPLOMATIC MISSIONS DEEP INTO THE OHIO COUNTRY.

AT TREATIES, HE WAS A CHIEF INTERPRETER. BECAUSE HE UNDERSTOOD THE SUBTLETIES OF THEIR SPEECH, THE CHIEFS' TRUST FOR THE DARK-EYED WHITE MAN GREW.

SOON, SIMON GIRTY, VALUED PUBLIC SERVANT, WAS ENTRUSTED TO TAKE THE SACRED OATH AS 2ND LIEUTENANT IN THE MILITIA...

"I, SIMON GIRTY, DO SINCERELY PROMISE AND SWEAR THAT I WILL BE FAITHFUL AND BEAR TRUE ALLEGIANCE TO HIS MAJESTY KING GEORGE III. SO HELP ME GOD...

"I DO DECLARE THAT THAT THERE IS NOT ANY TRANSUBSTANTIATION IN THE SACRAMENT OF THE LORD'S SUPPER SO HELP ME GOD...

"I, SIMON GIRTY, DO SWEAR FROM MY HEART TO ABHOR, DETEST, AND ABJURE AS IMPIOUS AND HERETICAL THE POPE OR ANY AUTHORITY OF THE SEE IN ROME. SO HELP ME GOD...

"I DO SINCERELY DECLARE THAT THE PERSON PRETENDED TO BE PRINCE OF WALES DURING THE LIFE OF THE LATE KING JAMES HATH NOT A SINGLE RIGHT OR TITLE WHATSOEVER TO THE CROWN...

"AND I DO SWEAR THAT I WILL BEAR FAITHFUL ALLIANCE TO HIS MAJESTY KING GEORGE III, AND DO MAKE THIS PROMISE HEARTILY, AND WILLINGLY, UPON THE TRUE FAITH OF A CHRISTIAN...

"... SO HELP ME GOD."

IT WAS THE FIRST TIME SIMON GIRTY EVER SET FOOT INSIDE A CHURCH...

ONE'S STANDING WITH GOD AND THE KING WAS NOW AN IMPORTANT ISSUE. HIS MAJESTY'S TREATMENT OF HIS AMERICAN SUBJECTS EARNED HIM SOME VERY VOCAL OPPONENTS.

DISSENT TURNED TO BLOODSHED. BLOODSHED LED TO OPEN REBELLION.

IN APRIL, 1775, BRITISH SOLDIERS WERE MET BY A CITIZEN'S ARMY AT LEXINGTON. AFTER 20 HOURS OF FIGHTING, THE REDCOATS MANAGED A MORTIFYING RETREAT.

BY JUNE, IT WAS CLEAR THAT THIS WAS NO SIMPLE PEASANTS' REBELLION. BRITISH TROOPS STORMED AN AMERICAN CAMP AT BUNKER'S HILL, AND 1,054 REDCOATS DIED.

THE TROUBLES SPILLED WESTWARD IN SEPTEMBER, THE REBELS TOOK CONTROL OF PITTSBURGH, AND CONNOLLY AND DUNMORE WERE SENT PACKING...

...LEAVING THOSE WHO HAD SIDED WITH THEM DURING THE TERRITORIAL SQUABBLES TO FEND FOR THEMSELVES!

GIRTY'S HOTHEADED FRIEND GEORGE ASTON WAS AMONGST THE FIRST CASUALTIES.

BY THE TIME THE CROWD WAS DONE WITH ASTON'S KILLER, THEY'D BROKEN BOTH HIS LEGS AND DRUG HIM THROUGH THE STREETS.

ALLIANCES WERE UNCERTAIN. OLD GRUDGES FESTERED AGAIN.

MOST OF THOSE WHO'D SIDED WITH PENNSYLVANIA DURING THE OLD BORDER TROUBLES WERE REGARDED AS GOOD PATRIOTS. BUT EVEN THOUGH GEORGE WASHINGTON HIMSELF HAD ONCE SYMPATHIZED WITH THEM, THE VIRGINIA MEN WERE VIEWED WITH SUSPICION!

THE FRONTIER WAS ABOUT TO BE SWEPT INTO THE PATH OF WAR. AND NO MATTER HOW HARD A MAN SEARCHED FOR IT, THERE WAS NO MIDDLE ROAD TO WALK...

THE WITCH HUNT BEGAN, AMIDST RUMORS OF A CONSPIRACY TO MURDER THE FORT'S GOOD PATRIOTS.

SIMON AND HIS FRIEND ALEXANDER MCKEE WERE JAILED. ALTHOUGH HE'D HELD A SEAT WITH THE PENNSYLVANIANS, MCKEE HADN'T BEEN VOCAL ENOUGH IN THE PATRIOT CAUSE.

HOWEVER, GIRTY SOON MADE A RATHER STYLISH ESCAPE-- BY CRAWLING THROUGH THE SEWER OF THE GUARD-HOUSE PRIVY!

AFTER SPENDING THE NIGHT IN A NEARBY ORCHARD...

...HE RETURNED TO THE GUARD-HOUSE TO AWAKEN HIS CAPTORS.

HE WAS ACQUITED OF HIS SUSPECTED CRIMES.

GIRTY STARTED WORKING FOR THE PATRIOTS, DRUMMING UP ENLISTMENTS FOR THE MILITIA. SOON, HOWEVER, HIS TALENTS AS A SPY AND DIPLOMAT WERE CALLED UPON ONCE AGAIN...

THE INDIANS HAD ATTACKED NEARBY FORT WHEELING, USING BRITISH GUNS AND AMMUNITION. THE SCOUT WAS SENT TO THE SENECA TRIBES TO IMPLORE THEM TO STAY NEUTRAL IN THE COMING CONFLICT.

THE IMPORTANT MISSION PROVED TO BE A THANKLESS TASK. GIRTY WAS NEARLY SLAIN BY THE SUSPICIOUS TRIBESMEN. MOST OF HIS EQUIPMENT AND PROVISIONS WERE LOST.

IN THE MIDDLE OF THE MISSION HE WAS DISMISSED-- FOR NO APPARENT REASON!

HE WAS NEVER COMPENSATED FOR HIS LOSSES. THE CAP-TAINCY THAT HE'D BEEN PROMISED WAS GIVEN TO ANOTHER MAN.

MOST OF GIRTY'S SUPERIORS WERE OLD PENNSYLVANIA MEN. THE MORE GIRTY TRIED TO ASSIST THE PATRIOTS, THE MORE SUSPICIONS HIS OLD ENEMIES LEVELLED AGAINST HIM.

TO THEM, EVERY IMPORTANT THING GIRTY HAD EVER DONE-- EVERY REASON HE HAD FOR EXISTING--

--BECAME WORTHLESS...

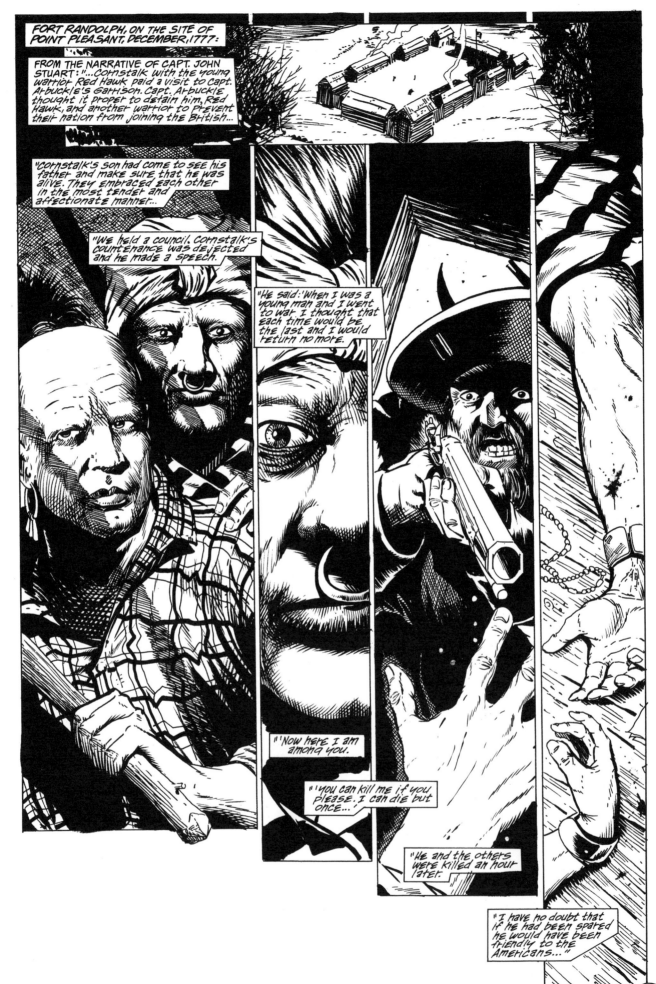

FORT RANDOLPH, ON THE SITE OF POINT PLEASANT, DECEMBER, 1777:

FROM THE NARRATIVE OF CAPT. JOHN STUART: "...Cornstalk with the young warrior Red Hawk paid a visit to Capt. Arbuckle's garrison. Capt. Arbuckle thought it proper to detain him, Red Hawk, and another warrior to prevent their nation from joining the British...

"Cornstalk's son had come to see his father and make sure that he was alive. They embraced each other in the most tender and affectionate manner...

"We held a council. Cornstalk's countenance was dejected and he made a speech.

"He said: 'When I was a young man and I went to war I thought that each time would be the last and I would return no more.

"'Now here I am among you.

"'You can kill me if you please. I can die but once...'

"He and the others were killed an hour later.

"I have no doubt that if he had been spared he would have been friendly to the Americans..."

15D

FEBRUARY, 1778, THE SALT LICKS ON THE MAHONING RIVER:

:uhhnnghh!:

GIRTY HAD BEEN HERE A LONG TIME AGO...

THE DELAWARE AND SENECA USED TO GATHER SALT AT THIS PLACE.

HE WAS JUST A BOY THEN...

...JUST A BOY...

THIS HERE BOY'S MINE, I SAY!

YOU'RE DAFT, CONNEL! WAS MY BALL WHAT DID HIM IN!

CONTENT YOURSELF WITH THE BLOODY SQUAWS!

LET'S LEAVE IT TO THE SCOUT, I SAY!

WHAT SAY YOU, GIRTY?! WHO GET'S THE HAIR?!

WELL?

CONNEL. CONNEL GETS THE HAIR.

IT HAD BEEN A LONG CAMPAIGN.

GENERAL HAND, THE NEW COMMANDER AT PITT, HAD LEARNED THAT THE BRITISH HAD STORED ARMS AT THE INDIAN VILLAGE OF CAYUGA. HE'D LAUNCHED A WINTER RAID, HOPING TO CATCH HIS ENEMIES BY SURPRISE.

SOON AFTER THE ARMY SET OUT, THE WEATHER HAD WARMED. THE WINTER SNOW MELTED. SUDDEN RAINS FLOODED THE CREEKS AND RIVERS AND TURNED THE GROUND INTO AN ANKLE-BREAKING, MUDDY SLUDGE.

HAND NEVER REACHED THE STORES AT CAYUGA.

©1989 TIMOTHY TRUMAN

470

THE WEARY AMERICANS HAD DISCOVERED A SMALL INDIAN VILLAGE. THEY EXPECTED TO FIND WARRIORS THERE. INSTEAD, THEY'D FOUND WOMEN, CHILDREN AND ONE OLD MAN.

THE DISAPPOINTED MILITIAMEN WOULDN'T COME HOME EMPTY-HANDED. THEY KILLED THE OLD MAN AND A WOMAN, AND TOOK ANOTHER WOMAN CAPTIVE.

THERE WERE SUPPOSED TO BE WARRIORS AT THE SALT LICK, TOO. GIRTY KNEW THE PLACE. HE LED THE PARTY THERE.

THE ONLY INDIANS THEY'D FOUND THERE WERE A BOY AND SOME WOMEN. CONNEL STILL HAD THE BOY'S SCALP...

THE EXPEDITION HAD BEEN A DISASTER. THE FOLKS AT PITT WERE ALREADY CALLING IT "HAND'S SQUAW CAMPAIGN."

THE PEOPLE THEY'D ATTACKED WERE DELAWARE -- ONE OF THE FEW TRIBES WHO HADN'T YET JOINED THE BRITISH.

MAYBE ALEXANDER MC KEE AND MATTHEW ELLIOTT WERE RIGHT...

THEY SAID THAT THE FRONTIERSMEN SAW EVERY RED MAN AS AN ENEMY. SO EVERY RED MAN HAD TO DIE.

WHERE WOULD THAT LEAVE A MAN LIKE SIMON GIRTY?

NOW, THE WITCH HUNTERS WERE PROWLING AGAIN. MC KEE AND ELLIOTT WERE UNDER CLOSE WATCH. EVEN GEORGE MORGAN WAS IN JAIL...

GEORGE? A TORY? SINCE MORGAN HAD BECOME THE FORT'S INDIAN AGENT, HE'D BEEN THE ONLY MAN TO KEEP THE DELAWARES ON THE AMERICANS' SIDE!

THINGS WERE BAD.

MAYBE IT WAS TIME TO MOVE ON... JUST AS SOON AS MORGAN WAS CLEARED...

TAKEN FROM THE LETTERS OF GENERAL EDWARD HAND AND DEPUTY INDIAN AGENT, GEORGE MORGAN, MARCH, 1778:

"...I am distressed to report that Mr. McKee escaped from here the night before last, accompanied by Mr. Matthew Elliott, Simon Girty, 2 others I am not acquainted with, and 2 negroes.

"Elliott had but a few weeks ago returned on parole from Detroit. I am told he possessed Mr. McKee's mind with the persuasion that McKee would be assassinated on the road to York, Pennsylvania.

"It is also probable that Elliott brought letters from the British in Canada that might have influenced McKee's conduct.

"Girty served as interpreter of the Six Nations' tongue at all the public treaties here. I think he will influence his brother, James, to join him. Evils might arise from the information these runaways can give the enemy.

"P.S.-Within this month 5 men have been killed, 2 wounded, and 4 taken by savages at Dunkard Creek."

SPRING WAS BREAKING. SOON IT WOULD BE SUMMER.

THE BIRDS WERE FLYING...

49D

PART 3 —
ACROSS THE BORDER

"Today, if ye will hear his voice,
harden not your hearts:
As in the provocation, as in the day
of temptation in the wilderness;
When your fathers tempted me,
proved me, and saw my works;
Forty years long was I grieved
in this generation, and said:
It is a people that do err
in their hearts, for they
have not known my ways;
Unto whom I sware my wrath,
that they should enter
into my rest."

— *English Prayer Book*

SEPTEMBER, 1778, NORTHERN KENTUCKY:

INSTRUCTIONS FROM THE BRITISH MINISTER TO GOVERNOR HAMILTON OF DETROIT:

"THERE CAN BE LITTLE DOUBT THAT THE INDIANS WILL READILY AND EAGERLY ENGAGE IN CRUSHING THE REBELLION AND RESTORING THE CONSTITION.

"IT IS THE KING'S COMMAND THAT YOU SHOULD ASSEMBLE AS MANY INDIANS AS YOU CONVENIENTLY CAN.

"PLACE PROPER PERSONS AT THEIR HEAD TO CONDUCT THEIR PARTIES, TO RESTRAIN THEM FROM COMMITTING VIOLENCE ON THE WELL-EFFECTED AND INOFFENSIVE INHABITANTS, ...

"... AND TO EMPLOY THEM IN MAKING A DIVERSION AND EXCITING AN ALARM UPON THE FRONTIERS.

"THIS MAY ENABLE YOU TO DIVIDE THE ATTENTION OF THE REBELS, THUS BRINGING THE WAR TO A MORE SPEEDY ISSUE AND RESTORING THOSE DELUDED PEOPLE TO THEIR FORMER STATE OF HAPPINESS, WHICH ARE THE FAVORITE ISSUES OF THE ROYAL BREAST."

CHAPTER 5

ACROSS THE OHIO RIVER...

...THE SHAWNEE TOWN OF WAPPATOMICA:

FOR THE SHAWNEES, IT HAD BEEN A GOOD RAID.

THE SCALPS OF 7 ENEMY MALES HAD BEEN TAKEN. THERE WERE 7 YOUNG ONES TO BE GIVEN TO THE LONELY MOTHERS WHO HAD LOST SONS TO THE LONG KNIVES, AND A GOOD WOMAN TO FILL A MAN'S LODGE WITH FOOD-SMOKE AND STRONG CHILDREN.

OR MAYBE THE BRITISHERS IN DETROIT WOULD BUY THE PRISONERS FROM THE SHAWNEE, PAYING IN GUNS AND GOODS AND STRONG WHISKEY...

51-E

IT WAS A GOOD DAY INDEED...

IN THE COUNCIL HOUSE WAS ANOTHER PRISONER -- A BIG, STRONG WHITE MAN WHO HAD BEEN CAUGHT STEALING HORSES.

HERE WAS A GREAT WARRIOR-- A FRIEND OF THE LONG KNIFE LEADER CLARK! ALTHOUGH HIS ARM HAD BEEN BROKEN, HE'D RUN THE GAUNTLET IN FOUR DIFFERENT VILLAGES AND LIVED!

WHEN THE CHILDREN HAD TORTURED HIM WITH HOT STICKS, HE'D KICKED A BOY INTO THE FIRE! TWICE, HIS SKULL HAD BEEN BROKEN! BUT, THE BIG WHITE MAN STILL LIVED!

HOW MANY MEN DOES CLARK HAVE IN KENTUCKY?

YES--THIS ONE MUST BE AN VALUED WARRIOR AMONG THE WHITES. SURELY HE COULD TELL THE BRITISH MANY IMPORTANT THINGS...

THESE BOYS ARE GOING TO BURN YOU, HORSE THIEF. YOU'D BEST TELL ME WHAT I WANT TO KNOW.

I... I DON'T KNOW...

...B-BUT I CAN GIVE YOU... THE NAMES AND RANKS... OF HIS... OFFICERS...

THAT'S AN OLD TRICK, SON. SOUNDS GOOD, BUT IT DOESN'T TELL ME A BLOODY THING.

YOU KNOW A FELLOW CALLED BILL STEWART?

...S-SURE... I KNOW 'IM.

MY LORD, SIMON... DON'T YOU RECOGNIZE ME...?

SWEET HEAVEN...

BUTLER...?!

THE CHIEFS DECIDED.

SIMON KENTON-- THE MAN WHO CALLED HIMSELF BUTLER... WOULD LIVE!

FOR THESE PEOPLE, THE PATH BETWEEN HATRED AND FRIENDSHIP, DEATH AND LIFE, WAS EASILY CROSSED. THE WARRIORS CROWDED AROUND KENTON, EACH CALLING HIM "BROTHER" EXPRESSING THEIR ADMIRATION OF HIS STRENGTH, HIS BRAVERY, HIS SPIRIT...

THEY CALLED HIM CUTTA-HO-THA-- "HE WHO WAS TO DIE"-- AND MADE HIM A SHAWNEE.

GIRTY TOOK HIS FRIEND INTO HIS HOME, CARED FOR HIS WOUNDS, GAVE HIM CLOTHES TO WEAR AND A HORSE TO RIDE...

THE BIG MAN HEALED QUICKLY. SOON, THEY WERE HUNTING TOGETHER AND VISITING THE SHAWNEE VILLAGES.

ONCE AGAIN, THE TWO MEN KNEW GOOD DAYS-- AND GIRTY HAD AN OLD FRIEND TO TALK TO...

THESE SHAWNEE ARE HARD TO UNDERSTAND, BUTLER. THEY LIVE DIFFERENT THAN WHITE FOLKS-- SO THEY HAVE TO THINK DIFFERENT.

I'VE SEEN SOME THINGS THAT HAVE MADE ME FEEL BAD. I'VE NEVER TAKEN THE SCALP OF A WHITE MAN OR A RED MAN. STILL-- THINGS AIN'T TURNED OUT LIKE I THOUGHT...

MAYBE...

...MAYBE I WAS TOO HASTY, BUTLER...

54E

THREE WEEKS LATER, IN THE SHAWNEE VILLAGE OF SOLOMON'S TOWN, EVERYTHING TURNED SOUR.

A GROUP OF WARRIORS LED BY A CHIEF NAMED REDPOLE RETURNED FROM A RAID IN KENTUCKY.

THINGS HAD NOT GONE WELL. THE LONG KNIFE SOLDIERS HAD DRAWN MUCH BLOOD FROM THEM.

REDPOLE, N'TSCHU!

<YES, GIR-TEE. I LIVE. BUT MANY OF OUR BRAVE MEN DIED. WE NEEDED YOUR GUN, MY BROTHER!>

HIYA, REDPOLE. IT'S -- UH -- IT'S GOOD TO SEE YOU...

KENTON OFFERED HIS HAND, BUT THE CHIEF REFUSED TO GRASP IT--A SERIOUS BREACH OF ETIQUETTE.

SOMETHING WAS VERY WRONG...

GIRTY WAS TO TAKE HIS FRIEND TO THE MAIN COUNCIL HOUSE AT WAPPATOMICA. THE WHITE MAN CALLED BUTLER WAS NO LONGER A BROTHER OF THE SHAWNEE! HIS LIFE WOULD BE PAYMENT FOR THEIR LOST WARRIORS.

AGAIN GIRTY PLEADED FOR KENTON'S LIFE. THIS TIME HE WAS ANGRILY REFUSED. GIRTY WASN'T A WAR LEADER-- ONLY A WATCHDOG WHO TURNED THE SHAWNEES' WORDS INTO ANIMAL LANGUAGE THAT THE BRITISH BARBARIANS COULD UNDERSTAND! IF HE INSISTED ON INTERFERING WITH COUNCIL'S WILL, HE AND HIS FRIEND WOULD BURN TOGETHER!

AT WAPPATOMICA IT WAS DECIDED: KENTON-- THE MAN CALLED BUTLER-- WOULD DIE.

AS A LAST RESORT, GIRTY HUMBLY SUGGESTED THAT KENTON BE TAKEN TO SANDUSKY, WHERE MANY TRIBES WERE ASSEMBLING TO RECIEVE THEIR ANNUAL GRATUITIES FROM THE BRITISH.

SANDUSKY WAS 50 MILES AWAY. PERHAPS THE JOURNEY WOULD BUY GIRTY TIME ENOUGH TO SPEAK TO ALEXANDER MCKEE. AS BRITISH INDIAN OFFICER, MCKEE'S INFLUENCE WITH THE TRIBES WAS GREAT...

SADLY, MCKEE COULD DO NOTHING.

68

JANUARY, 1779, FT. LAURENS:

THE BRITISH SENT GIRTY WITH A GROUP OF MINGOES DEEP INTO THE OHIO WILDERNESS, TO OBSERVE TROOP MOVEMENTS AND CAUSE MISCHIEF AROUND THE REBELS' NEW FORT THERE.

IT WAS GIRTY'S FIRST MILITARY MISSION AGAINST THE AMERICAN ARMY...

THINGS DIDN'T GO AS PLANNED...

CHIEF KILLBUCK'S DELAWARES WERE STILL SEEKING FRIENDSHIP WITH THE AMERICANS AND HAD ASKED A GROUP OF WHITE MISSIONARIES TO WARN THE PATRIOTS OF THE ATTACK. THE MINGOES CONTENTED THEMSELVES WITH ATTACKING THE FORT'S SUPPLY WAGONS.

THE COMMANDER AT LAURENS WAS JOHN GIBSON-- THE SAME MAN WHO, 5 YEARS BEFORE, HAD WRITTEN DOWN GIRTY'S TRANSLATION OF LOGAN'S SPEECH.

JOHN "HORSEFACE" GIBSON... THAT LONG-JOWLED RASCAL...!

HE'D BEEN A PENNSYLVANIA MAN DURING THE TROUBLE AT FORT PITT. GIRTY'S OLD ENEMIES HAD MADE SURE THAT GIBSON HAD DONE WELL.

NOW GIBSON WAS BOASTING THAT HE ALONE HAD GOTTEN THE SPEECH FROM LOGAN... AND THAT HE'D PERSONALLY KILL GIRTY IF HE CAUGHT HIM!

SO--OLD "HORSEFACE" WANTED HIS SCALP, DID HE? SO THAT'S THE WAY IT WAS GOING TO BE?

THEN SO BE IT...

© 1989 TIMOTHY [signature]

57E

GIRTY STILL HAD NO MILITARY COMMISSION WITH THE BRITISH. BUT IN THE EYES OF THE WHITE PATRIOTS, THE INDIANS WERE UNDISCIPLINED, UNEDUCATED SAVAGES WHO COULDN'T POSSIBLY BE LEADING THEIR OWN ATTACKS...

THUS, GIRTY BECAME A MAN WITH A PRICE ON HIS HEAD.

$800. WAS A LOT OF MONEY...

SOONER OR LATER, SOMEONE WOULD TRY TO COLLECT IT...

SO... THE DELAWARES WERE AFTER HIS SCALP, TOO...

DID THEY THINK THAT THE AMERICANS WERE COUNTING THE FAVORS THAT THE DELAWARES DID FOR THEM?

SOMEDAY, THE WHITE GOVERNMENT WOULD TURN ON THEM, JUST LIKE THEY HAD THE REST.

SOMEBODY WAS KEEPING THE DELAWARES FROM JOINING THE WAR...

SOMEBODY WAS HELPING THE DELAWARES TO WORK AGAINST THE OTHER TRIBES...

...AND, BY HEAVEN, SOMEBODY WAS SAYING SOME VERY BAD THINGS ABOUT SIMON GIRTY!

JULY, 1779...

...A SMALL PATH NEAR THE MORAVIAN MISSION OF LICHTENAU:

NO...

STAND EASY, BROTHER ISSAC...

<THERE, MY BROTHERS-- THAT'S THE VERY MAN WE'VE COME FOR!>

<THAT'S THE SPY, DAVID ZEISBERGER!>

<TAKE HIM, BROTHERS! KEEP THE PROMISE YOU HAVE MADE TO ME!>

<GIR-TEE! LISTEN! SOMEONE ELSE IS COMING!>

<LEAVE THIS MAN WHO DRESSES LIKE A WOMAN! WE MUST GO!>

THE MINGOES MELTED INTO THE FOREST. REVEREND DAVID ZEISBERGER WAS SAFE... FOR NOW.

SIMON GIRTY WOULD SOON HAVE OTHER THINGS TO OCCUPY HIMSELF WITH...

59E

...THE NEXT FEW YEARS WERE GOING TO BE A VERY BLOODY TIME...

GEORGE GIRTY HAD NOW JOINED HIS BROTHERS.

FOR TWO YEARS HE'D SERVED WITH THE PATRIOTS' MARINES ABOARD A RIDICULOUS ARMED FLATBOAT CALLED "THE RATTLETRAP." HIS BROTHERS' GROWING INFAMY HAD CAUSED HIM SOME TROUBLE...

SO, IN FALL, 1778, HE JOINED SIMON AND FELLOW RENEGADE MATTHEW ELLIOTT ON THE OHIO.

BROTHER GEORGE HAD LEARNED A LOT WITH THE MARINES...

IN OCTOBER, THEY AMBUSHED A FLOTILLA OF BATTEAUS NEAR THE MOUTH OF THE LITTLE MIAMI RIVER. THE BOATS WERE LOADED WITH GUNPOWDER, PURCHASED FROM THE SPANISH AND BOUND FOR GENERAL CLARK'S KENTUCKIANS.

COMMANDING THE BOATS WAS DAVID RODGERS.

TOO BAD... "OLD DAVE" HAD BEEN A MEMBER OF THE VIRGINIA FACTION DURING THE BORDER DISPUTES.

NOT THAT GIRTY HAD LIKED HIM MUCH...

THE GIRTYS SPENT THE WINTER IN DETROIT. BUT IN THE EARLY SUMMER, THEY WERE CALLED ON AGAIN...

CAPTAIN BIRD WAS LEADING A MASSIVE FORCE OF 150 BRITISH SOLDIERS AND 700 INDIANS IN AN ORGANIZED MILITARY STRIKE AGAINST THE KENTUCKY FORTS. THE GIRTYS WOULD SERVE AS INTERPRETERS.

IT WAS AN IMPORTANT AND DIFFICULT ASSIGNMENT. THE INDIANS CAME FROM DIFFERENT TRIBES, EACH WITH ITS OWN LANGUAGE.

AND, OF COURSE, THE BRITISH AND THEIR ALLIES DIFFERED GREATLY IN THEIR OPINIONS ON JUST HOW A WAR SHOULD BE CONDUCTED...

RUDDLE'S STATION IN KENTUCKY, JUNE, 1780:

GIRTY HIMSELF HAD CONVINCED THE CAPTAIN OF THE FORT TO OPEN THE GATES. THE RENEGADE HAD PROMISED THE SETTLERS SAFETY FROM BIRD'S CANNON AND THE INDIANS' KNIVES.

IN THE PAST, GIRTY HAD DICTATED LETTERS TO THE BRITISH COMMANDERS, ASKING FOR OFFICERS TO BE SENT WITH THE INDIANS ON THEIR RAIDS TO SEE THAT INNOCENTS DIDN'T SUFFER...

...FOR SIMON GIRTY KNEW THAT THE FOREST PEOPLE MADE WAR A TERRIBLE THING FOR THEIR ENEMIES.

AT LAST, THE BRITISH HAD SENT BIRD...

...AND BIRD HAD FAILED.

ON THE WAY BACK TO DETROIT, SIMON GIRTY LEFT THE BRITISH TO LIVE IN THE VILLAGES OF THE WYANDOTTS.

LITTLE WAS HEARD FROM HIM FOR ALMOST A YEAR...

IN THE MEANTIME, WHAT GIRTY KNEW WOULD HAPPEN DID HAPPEN...

VENGEANCE WAS FOLLOWED WITH VENGEANCE. CLARK'S LONG KNIVES SOON PLUNGED DEEP INTO THE OHIO WILDERNESS AND KILLED EVERY INDIAN ENCOUNTERED!

THE SHAWNEES BURNED THEIR OWN CAPITAL, CHILLICOTHE, RATHER THAN ALLOWING IT TO FALL INTO CLARK'S HANDS.

THE PEOPLE OF PIQUA WERE LESS FORTUNATE...

GEORGE AND JAMES GIRTY FOUGHT SIDE-BY-SIDE WITH ITS DEFENDERS, AND BARELY MANAGED TO FLEE WITH ITS SURVIVORS INTO THE WILDERNESS.

THE WRATH OF THE LONG KNIVES DIDN'T END WITH THOSE WHO'D ASSISTED BIRD IN THE BUTCHERY AT RUDDLE'S STATION...

IN MARCH, 1781, THE DELAWARES HAD SEVERED ALL RELATIONS WITH THE AMERICANS.

ONE MONTH LATER, THE AMERICANS DESTROYED THE DELAWARE CAPITAL OF COSHOCTON...

61E

FROM SIMON GIRTY'S REPORT TO BRITISH GENERAL DE PEYSTER, APRIL, 1781:

"Went to Coshocton with twenty Wyandotts...

"Colonel Broadhead, with 500 Americans, have burned the town and killed 15 men. He took the women and children prisoner but afterwards let them go.

"Broadhead told the Delaware that he will beat all the Indians out of this country. Even now, Colonel George Rogers Clark is on the Ohio with another 1,000 Americans.

"The Wyandotts with me would be very glad if you sent the men you promised. The Christian Indians at the Moravian Missions have asked for us to help them flee before the rebels come.

"I have 160 Indians at this place. Their provisions are gone. They beg you to send more.

"I would also be obliged, sir, if you send a little provisions for myself, as I gave mine to the Indians."

THINGS WERE BEGINNING TO GO VERY BADLY FOR THE TRIBES. THE REBELS WERE GETTING TOO CLOSE.

THE INDIANS FOUGHT BACK AS BEST THEY COULD, RAIDING SETTLEMENTS TO SECURE PROVISIONS FOR THEIR OWN FAMILIES.

THEY WERE ALSO BRINGING BACK CAPTIVES. MOST OF THESE PRISONERS WERE BEING BURNED.

DESPITE THE RUMORS THAT GIRTY WAS A MAJOR WAR LEADER, THE RENEGADE ACTUALLY HAD LITTLE AUTHORITY AMONGST THE TRIBES.

HE WAS AN INTERPRETER AND SCOUT. HE DIDN'T DETERMINE INDIAN WAR POLICY--AND HE COULDN'T COMMAND CHIEFS TO RELEASE THEIR PRISONERS.

BUT SOMETIMES, WHEN SEVERAL CAPTIVES HAD BEEN TAKEN AND THE WARRIORS HAD BEEN ABLE TO SATISFY THEIR AWFUL VENGEANCE, AN OCCASIONAL PRISONER COULD BE BARGAINED FOR.

MANY OF THEM-- LIKE YOUNG HENRY BAKER OF WHEELING-- OWED SIMON GIRTY THEIR LIVES.

THE BAKER BOY WOULD NOT BE THE LAST TO BE FREED...

NOR WOULD THE UNFORTUNATE MEN WHO HAD BEEN CAPTURED WITH HIM TO BE THE LAST TO DIE...

AUGUST 24, 1781. THE OHIO RIVER, NEAR THE MOUTH OF THE GREAT MIAMI:

IT WAS A TIME OF GREAT DANGER. THE WHITE LONG KNIVES WERE COMING-- AND THEY WERE ANGRY.

CHAPTER 6

TOO MANY OF THEIR SETTLEMENTS HAD BEEN BURNED BY INDIAN RAIDING PARTIES. TOO MANY FRIENDS HAD DIED SCREAMING AT THE STAKE. TOO MANY CHILDREN HAD BEEN STOLEN FROM THEIR FIELDS.

NOW, SIMON GIRTY, HIS BROTHER GEORGE, AND CHIEF JOSEPH BRANT--WAR LEADER OF THE IROQUOIS-- WATCHED FOR SIGNS OF THE APPROACHING AVENGERS...

GEORGE ROGERS CLARK AND HIS LONG KNIVES WERE MARCHING DEEP INTO THE OHIO COUNTRY!

BUT CLARK'S GREAT ARMY WOULD NEED MORE THAN HATRED TO SUSTAIN IT. HIS MEN WOULD NEED FLOUR FOR THEIR BELLIES AND GUNPOWDER FOR THEIR TERRIBLE CANNONS.

THEIR ENEMIES WERE DETERMINED THAT SUCH NEEDS WOULD NEVER BE FULFILLED.

IT HAD BEEN A GREAT VICTORY.

THE SUPPLY BOATS HAD BEEN COMMANDED BY ARCHIBALD LOCHRY--ONE OF GIRTY'S OLDEST ENEMIES FROM THE FORT PITT DAYS. LOCHRY HAD BEEN A STAUNCH PENNSYLVANIA MAN. THE REBELS HAD MADE HIM A CAPTAIN.

WHO KNEW WHAT THE DEVIL WOULD DO WITH HIM?

HIS BOATS WERE LOADED WITH SPANISH POWDER, BOUGHT IN NEW ORLEANS AND BOUND FOR CLARK'S ARMY. ALMOST 100 WHITE SOLDIERS HAD BEEN SLAIN. THE LONG KNIVES HAD BEEN DEALT A CRIPPLING BLOW.

IT WAS CAUSE FOR CELEBRATION.

...I, CHIEF JOSEPH BRANT-- THAYENDENAGA OF THE MOHAWKS --AM A GREAT MAN!

I HAVE MET KINGS AND IN THE STREETS OF LONDON! I HAVE TRANSLATED THE HOLY BOOKS OF JEHOVAH FOR MY PEOPLE! MANY TIMES HAVE I LED MY RED BROTHERS AGAINST THE INVADERS!

AND NOW, I HAVE NIPPED THE NOSE OF OUR GREAT ENEMY, GENERAL CLARK, HIMSELF! INDEED, I'VE DONE A FINE THING THIS DAY...!

YOU LYIN', SANCTIMONIOUS DOG!

'TWAS MY BROTHER, GEORGE, WHO MADE THE PLAN! THE HONOR BELONGS TO HIM-- AND NONE OTHER!

FILTHY SOT! I AM CHIEF TO THE MOHAWKS!

NO ONE SPEAKS TO ME IN SUCH A MANNER!

uuhhhh!

BRANT'S SABER HAD BITTEN DEEPLY. THE WOUND WAS SEVERE.

GIRTY WOULD BEAR ITS SCAR ON HIS FOREHEAD FOR THE REST OF HIS DAYS...

THE RENEGADE WAS CARRIED AWAY TO RECOVER--TO CHIEF HALF KING'S TOWN ON THE UPPER SANDUSKY...

64F

BUT, DURING HIS MONTHS OF RECUPERATION, GIRTY DISCOVERED THAT HE WAS NOT THE ONLY WHITE MAN LIVING WITH THE STARVING WYANDOTTS OF THE UPPER SANDUSKY...

ZEISBERGER! DAVID ZEISBERGER!

SO! YOUR MISSION INDIANS WON'T STAND AND FIGHT, SO YOU FOLLOWED THE FLEEING RASCALS HERE!

WHAT'S ON THE PLATE, REVEREND? I'VE DRANK MY FILL OF RANK TRADE WHISKEY TO EASE THIS PAIN IN MY SKULL, AND NOW I'VE A HOLE IN MY BELLY THAT NEEDS FILLIN'!

I'M SURE THAT YOU'LL FIND CHARITY IN YOUR HEART AND LET US SHARE IN YOUR BOUNTY!

ALL TOLD, GIRTY'S CONVALESCENCE WASN'T QUITE AS BORING AS HE'D ORIGINALLY FEARED...

DESPITE SUCH DIVERSIONS, WINTER WAS HARSH. CHIEF HALF KING'S PEOPLE WERE STARVING. HE DEMANDED THAT THE BRITISH COMMANDER IN DETROIT REMOVE THE MISSIONARIES, THEIR DIS-PLACED FLOCK, AND THEIR STRANGE TEACHINGS...

BY APRIL, GIRTY HAD RECOVERED, AND WAS ASSIGNED TO BRING THE MORAVIANS TO DETROIT.

HOWEVER, BEFORE THEY COULD DEPART, GIRTY WAS CALLED TO ACCOMPANY A RAID ON THE OHIO SETTLE-MENTS. HE ASKED A RENEGADE FRENCHMAN TO TAKE HIS PLACE, ORDERING HIM TO DRIVE THE MORAVIANS LIKE CATTLE TO THE BRITISH STRONGHOLD.

THE WEARY REFUGEES STOPPED AT A TRAD-ING POST TO REST AND WAIT FOR THE SPRING STORM-SEASON TO PASS SO THAT THEY COULD RESUME THEIR JOURNEY...

UNFORTUNATELY, THEY WERE STILL THERE WHEN GIRTY RETURNED FROM THE OHIO RAID...

65F

MR. LE VILLIERS! I ORDERED YOU TO WHIP THESE SOUL-SUCKERS TO DETROIT!

WHAT ARE YOU DOING STOPPED HERE?!!

SEE HERE, GIRTY! ZEISBERGER IS ILL! BROTHER HECKEWELDER IS 60-YEARS-OLD! THEIR CONVERTS ARE EXHAUSTED! THEY'D NEVER SURVIVE A--

SECURE A BOAT! STORM OR NO STORM, YOU'RE GETTIN' THIS BLEEDIN' BAGGAGE TO DETROIT!

DO IT-- OR, BY HEAVEN, I'LL TOMAHAWK THEM NOW!

BLOODY DEMON...

BOY?

BOY? WHAT IS WRONG?

NO. THAT'S NOT IT.

YOU'RE A CAPTIVE, AREN'T YOU? YOU'RE THINKING OF HOME...

N-NOTHING, SIR...!

MY NAME IS CHRISTIAN FAST. I... I HAVE NO... FRIENDS HERE! I'M... LONELY...

THE GNUDENHUTTEN MASSACRE WAS SCORNED BY GOVERNMENT OFFICIALS. BUT TO THOSE WHO'D LOST LOVED ONES TO THE INDIANS, WILLIAMSON AND HIS MEN WERE HEROES.

HALF THE FRONTIER MARSHALED TO WILLIAMSON'S CALL FOR A NEW EXPEDITION. THE MAN WHO LED THIS GREAT ARMY WOULD BECOME A VERY FAMOUS MAN.

GIRTY'S OLD LANDLORD, COLONEL WILLIAM CRAWFORD, GLADLY ACCEPTED THE POSITION.

MANY IMPORTANT PEOPLE WERE INTERESTED IN CRAWFORD'S SUCESS. EVEN GENERAL WASHINGTON HIMSELF OWED MANY FAVORS TO THE MAN WHO ONCE HAD BEEN HIS FAITHFUL LAND AGENT.

YES-- COLONEL WILLIAM CRAWFORD WOULD INDEED GO FAR.

THE INDIANS COULD NOT HOPE TO STAND AGAINST SUCH A GREAT ARMY.

NO QUARTER TO SAVAGES

FROM THE BEGINNING, CRAWFORD'S MEN MADE THEIR INTENTIONS FOR THE RED PEOPLE VERY CLEAR.

HOWEVER, THINGS DIDN'T GO QUITE AS THE WHITE MEN HAD EXPECTED.

THE INDIANS HAD LEARNED THE ENEMY'S PLAN, AND RESERVED A SPECIAL FATE FOR THOSE WHO HAD MURDERED THEIR PEACEFUL BROTHERS AND SISTERS AT GNUDENHUTTEN.

THEIR VICTORY OVER THE WHITE DEVIL WILLIAMSON AND THE DOG WHO LED HIS ARMY WOULD BE GRAND...

...THE DEATHS OF THESE MURDERERS WOULD BE SPECTACULAR!

CAUGHT BETWEEN HALF KING'S WYANDOTTS, CAPTAIN PIPE'S DELAWARES AND SHAWNEES, AND 100 BRITISH RANGERS, CRAWFORD'S GREAT EXPEDITION WAS UTTERLY CRUSHED IN THE FIELDS OF MINGO BOTTOM...

THE NEXT DAY, COLONEL WILLIAM CRAWFORD, 5 OF HIS SOLDIERS, AND THE DIVISION SURGEON, DR. KNIGHT, WERE MARCHED TO CAPTAIN PIPE'S TOWN ON LITTLE TYMOCHTEE CREEK.

EVENTUALLY, THE 5 SOLDIERS WERE TOMAHAWKED AND SCALPED BY A GROUP OF WOMEN AND BOYS.

AS THE TERRIFIED DOCTOR WATCHED, CRAWFORD WAS LED TO THE STAKE...

...AND THEN HIS TORTURE BEGAN.

G-GIRTY-- FOR GOD'S SAKE...

...uhhnnh...

...P. PLEASE... SH-SHOOT ME!!

CAN'T YOU SEE, COLONEL?

I HAVE NO GUN.

HAHAHAHAHAHAHAHAHAHAHA

IT TOOK WILLIAM CRAWFORD MANY HOURS TO DIE...

YOUR BIG COLONEL'S ALREADY NEAR DEATH, DR. KNIGHT.

THEY'RE GOING TO TAKE YOU TO THE SHAWNEE TOWNS. THE SHAWNEES, I THINK, WILL TREAT YOU IN LIKE MANNER.

I ONLY WISH THAT "HORSEFACE" JOHN GIBSON WAS HERE. I'D LIGHT THE BLASTED TORCH MYSELF.

AYE-- GIBSON HAS INSULTED ME GREATLY OVER THE YEARS.

YOUR SOLDIERS TOLD ME THAT IF I EVER FELL INTO YOUR PEOPLE'S HANDS, I'D BE TREATED KINDLY.

WHAT DO YOU THINK, DR. KNIGHT?

HAH! DO YOU KNOW WHAT I THINK?

...I THINK THAT THEY'D ROAST ME ALIVE, WITH FAR MORE PLEASURE THAN THOSE DEVILS ARE GETTING FROM BROILING THE COLONEL!

"WHAT'S YOUR OPINION, DR. KNIGHT...?"

"... DO YOU THINK THEY'D BE GLAD TO SEE ME DIE?..."

72F

ONE YEAR LATER...

PENNSYLVANIA, MAY, 1783. A MOUNTAIN NEAR PITTSBURGH AND THE SETTLEMENT OF NINE-MILE RUN...:

IT HAD BEEN A LONG WINTER.

THE LONG KNIFE SOLDIERS HAD BURNED THE CORNFIELDS AND FOOD STORES OF THE SOUTHERN OHIO TRIBES. THE FAMILES OF THE SHAWNEES, THE DELAWARES, THE MIAMIS, THE MINGOES, THE SENECAS, THE MOHAWKS, AND THE WYANDOTTS WERE STARVING.

SO THE INDIANS CONTINUED THEIR MIGRATION WESTWARD-- TO THE BRITISH AT DETROIT.

MANY HAD DIED-- OF WAR, OF COLD, OF HUNGER...

BUT THOSE WHO LIVED SWORE TO CARRY THE FIGHT BACK TO THE AMERICANS. THEIR VICTORY OVER CRAWFORD ON THE SANDUSKY HAD TAUGHT THEM THAT THEY COULD STILL WIN.

YES--THEY HAD BURNED MANY WHITE SOLDIERS AFTER THAT BATTLE...

DR. KNIGHT-- WHO HAD WITNESSED COLONEL CRAWFORD'S TORTURE --HAD ESCAPED!

DR. KNIGHT HAD WRITTEN A BOOK DETAILING HIS HARROWING CAPTIVITY AND HIS COMMANDER'S GRISLY DEATH. THE BOOK WAS AN INSTANT SUCCESS...

AND EVERY TIME IT WAS READ, THE BRUTALIZED GHOST OF COLONEL WILLIAM CRAWFORD WOULD RISE FROM THE ASHES TO THRUST A BONY FINGER AT THOSE RESPONSIBLE FOR HIS SUFFERING.

INEVITABLY, THAT FINGER POINTED TO ONE MAN: A DEPRAVED, WICKED "WHITE SAVAGE" WHO SAT IN THE MIDST OF THE ENEMY AND WATCHED A FELLOW WHITE MAN DIE...

73F

HIS NAME WAS SIMON GIRTY...

...AND ON THE DAY HE WAS BORN,
HE ENTERED THE WILDERNESS.

THIS VOLUME DEDICATED TO EDDIE SEACRIST, JR., MY
BLOOD KIN, FOR THE DAYS WHEN WE WALKED THE SAME
TRAILS AS GIRTY AND KENTON, WITHOUT EVEN
KNOWING IT...

© 1989
TIMOTHY
TRUMAN

END OF BOOK ONE

"SIMON GIRTY: 1778"

The new lithograph from Timothy Truman

The newest in a series of historical prints from Timothy Truman features Simon Girty, whose tumultuous true-life story is the subject of the artist's *Wilderness* graphic novel

    Captured and raised by Seneca Indians while a boy, Simon Girty was later released to the Colonial garrison at Fort Pitt, where he earned a reputation as a trusted scout, interpreter, and frontier hero during Governor Dunmore's war preceding the American Revolution. But in March of 1778 Girty and government Indian agents Alexander McKee and Matthew Elliot deserted the American regiment at Pittsburg and joined the English and their Native American allies at Fort Detroit. Within months the "White Savage" was seen leading Indian raids on forts and settlements in Ohio, Pennsylvania, Kentucky, and West Virginia.
    In *Simon Girty: 1778* , Truman has attempted to capture the decision that led Girty to leave his own people and become the most controversial and vilified renegade in the history of the American Frontier.

    This print is a perfect reproduction of Truman's original, intricate pencil rendering, and is printed on the highest-quality, acid-free, bristol-weight paper in a signed and numbered edition.

    This limited edition specialty item will be shipped to comics distributors, retailers, and select fine-arts and historical market outlets in JULY, 1989. It is also available directly from 4Winds Publishing Group, Inc., by sending $40 (plus $3 shipping and handling) to:

4Winds Publishing Group, Inc.
P.O. Box 5208
Lancaster, Pa. 17601
Pennsylvania residents please add sales tax.